OXFORD *Playscripts*

Lucas

Steve Barlow & Steve Skidmore

Paper Tigers

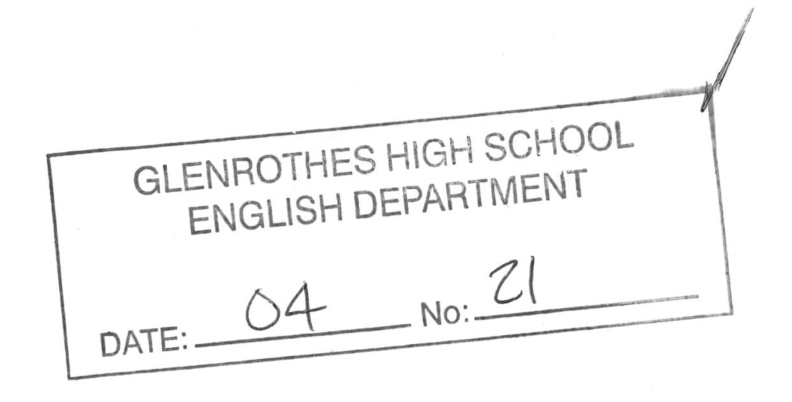

Oxford University Press

OXFORD
UNIVERSITY PRESS

Great Clarendon Street, Oxford OX2 6DP

Oxford University Press is a department of the University of Oxford.
It furthers the University's objective of excellence in research, scholarship,
and education by publishing worldwide in

Oxford New York

Auckland Bangkok Buenos Aires Cape Town Chennai
Dar es Salaam Delhi Hong Kong Istanbul Karachi Kolkata
Kuala Lumpur Madrid Melbourne Mexico City Mumbai
Nairobi São Paulo Shanghai Taipei Tokyo Toronto

Oxford is a registered trade mark of Oxford University Press
in the UK and in certain other countries

First published 1991

British Library Cataloguing in Publication Data

Data available

ISBN 0 19 831268 7

20 19 18 17 16 15 14 13 12 11

Illustrated by Phillip Burrows

Typeset at Pentacor, High Wycombe, Bucks

Printed and bound in China

Contents

Introduction

The Do-It-Yourself Section

In each play you will find a 'DIY' Section. We have put this in so that you have the chance to put forward *your* ideas. You will be asked to make up some scenes about the characters and the situations they find themselves in. To get you thinking, we have suggested some scenes you could explore, but we hope that you will think of your own. (They'll probably be better than ours, anyway!)

When you are reading the plays and get to the DIY Section, you have a choice. You can either skip this and go on to the next scene or begin to work on your ideas.

If you decide to skip the section, don't worry about missing out on the storyline; we have written the plays so that you will not lose the thread of the plot.

If you decide to work on the DIY Section, you can choose to present your ideas in several ways.

Improvisation

You can read about how to set up an improvisation in the Activities section on page 147. In small groups, you can work out your ideas and when you are happy with them, write down what happens and what the characters say. This is called **scripting**. You can then practise your scenes and, when you are happy with them, share them with the other members of your group.

Film and Video

If you have the equipment available, you could film your improvisations on movie film or videotape. This can be exciting as you might be able to do location work by actually filming your work out of school or college. You might even wish to film some of the scenes we have written, with members of the group taking the parts of the characters in the plays.

Radio Play

If you don't have access to film or video equipment, you can produce a radio play instead, using a cassette recorder. Remember that anybody who listens to the play cannot see what is going on, so you will have to help your audience to understand what is happening by using sound effects and detailed descriptions.

Photostory

By using a camera, you can produce a photostory, like the ones you read in comics and magazines. Improvise some scenes and then decide which moments in the scenes you wish to photograph. Plan out your pictures first by producing a **storyboard**. This tells the story in a series of still images, like a still cartoon. (Don't worry about how good your drawing is, stick figures will do fine.) You must do this first, so that you know that the audience will understand the plot. Once you have planned this out, you can take a camera and photograph the scenes.

If you use prints, you could present your story by putting them up on the wall, and writing the words that the characters say underneath the pictures.

If you use slides, you could put on a slide show and record the characters' words on a cassette tape and play this as you show the slides. You can make this type of presentation even more interesting by recording background music on the tape.

These are just a few of the different ways you can use the DIY Section. Think of other ways of presenting your ideas. Be as inventive as possible and don't be afraid to experiment. Most of all, we want you to *enjoy* working on the plays.

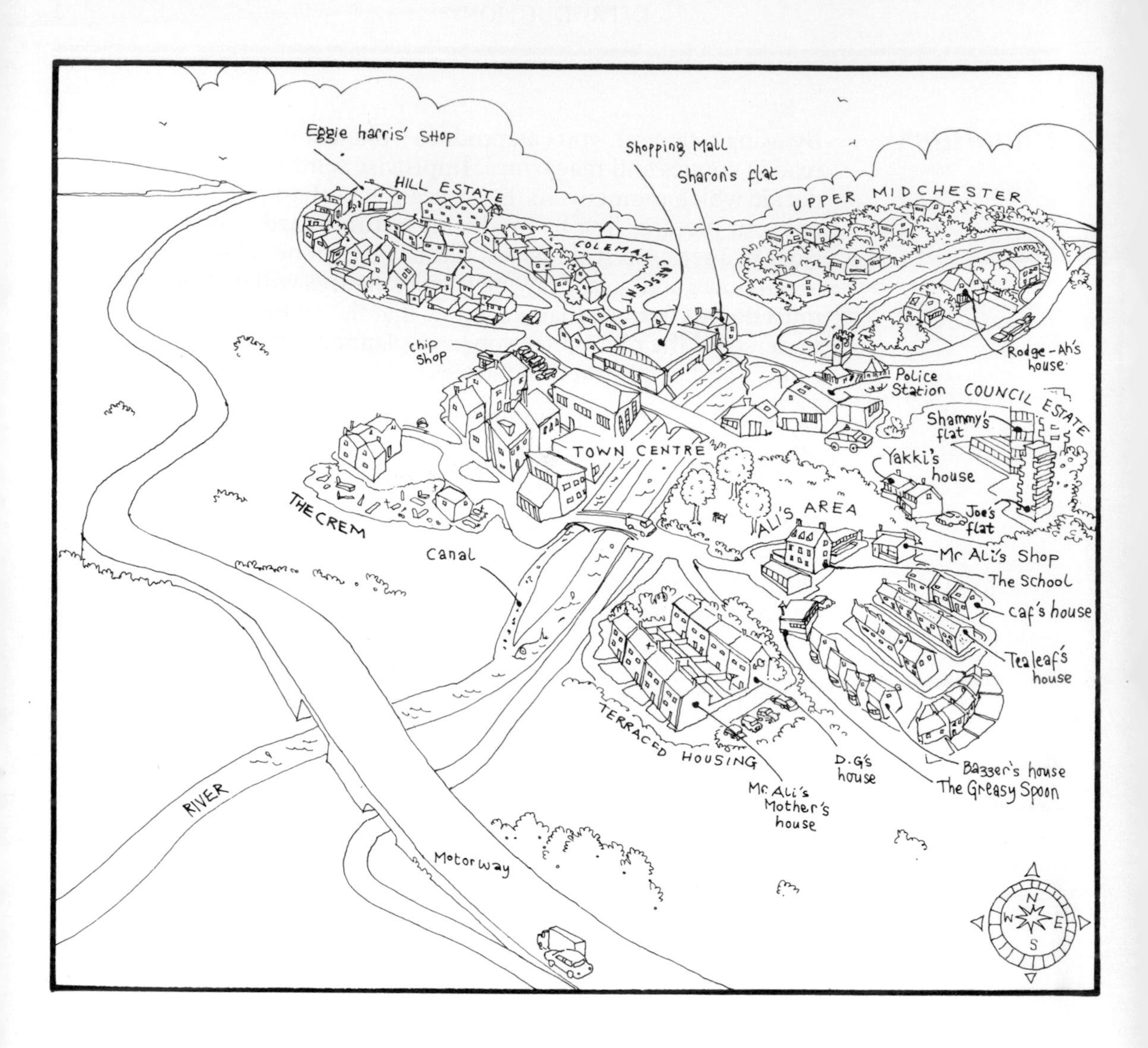

Eggie harris' Shop
HILL ESTATE
Shopping Mall
Sharon's flat
UPPER MIDCHESTER
COLEMAN CRESCENT
Rodge-Ah's house
Chip Shop
Police Station
COUNCIL ESTATE
Shammy's flat
Yakki's house
TOWN CENTRE
Joe's flat
ALI'S AREA
THE CREM
Canal
Mr Ali's Shop
The School
caf's house
Tealeaf's house
TERRACED HOUSING
D.G's house
Bazzer's house
The Greasy Spoon
Mr. Ali's Mother's house
RIVER
Motorway
N
W
E
S

Paper Tigers

The Characters

Mr Ali	*the owner of the paper shop*
Gareth	*a newcomer*
Caf	
DG	
Shammy	
Sharon	
Kawasaki Joe	*the 'Paper Tigers'*
Rodge-ah	
Bazzer	
Tealeaf	
Mrs Green	*the previous owner of the shop*
Police 1	*the long-suffering local Law.* *
Police 2	

* NB The police could be either men or women.

Scene 1

Inside the back room of the paper shop. **Mr Ali** *is checking through some magazines and numbering them. He puts some of the magazines into the paper round shoulder bags. He hums to himself.*

Gareth *enters the room. He looks around nervously.*

Gareth Er . . . hello?

Mr Ali *turns quickly and stares at Gareth.*

Gareth Er . . . there was no one in the shop, and I heard you hummin' in here . . .

Mr Ali I didn't hear the bell.

Gareth Perhaps it's not working.

Mr Ali *(Relaxing a little)* Perhaps not. What can I do for you?

Gareth You are Mr Ali, aren't you?

Mr Ali I am. And you?

Gareth *(Confused)* No, I'm not Mr Ali . . . oh I see! Sorry! I'm Gareth. Gareth Davies. I've come about the job. On the window outside. The paper round job.

Mr Ali Ah, the job. Have you done a paper round before?

Gareth No.

Mr Ali Oh. Do you know the area well?

Gareth No.

Mr Ali Oh. Well, thank you for coming to see me, Gareth, but I'm afraid . . .

Gareth We only just moved here, see, a month ago.

Mr Ali I see. Where did you move from?

Gareth Criccieth.

Mr Ali Criccieth?

Gareth *(Patiently)* It's in Wales.

Mr Ali Yes, I know. North Wales. Near Porthmadog, isn't it?

Gareth *(Shocked)* How do you know that?

Mr Ali No need to look so astonished. I've been there . . . for my holidays. A delightful place. So, you're new here.

Gareth Yeah, but if you gave me a job, I'd find my way round dead quick . . . honest!

Mr Ali Well, I'll tell you what I'll do. Theresa is sick at the moment. Do her round tonight and see how you get on.

Gareth Right! Thanks!

There is a noise outside.

Mr Ali Ah! That'll be the Tigers.

Gareth What! Do you keep tigers?

Mr Ali *(Laughing)* No, that's just my name for the boys and girls who deliver papers for me.

Enter ***Caf****,* ***Double Glazing*** *(****DG****), Shamir (known as* ***Shammy****), and* ***Sharon****. They chatter away to each other before realizing that there is a new person. They eye Gareth suspiciously.*

Mr Ali Hello, Cathy, DG, Shamir, Sharon.

DG Good evening.

Shammy Hello.

Sharon Hi.

Caf *ignores Mr Ali. She continues to look at Gareth.*

Mr Ali We've got a new person. I'd like you to meet him.

Kawasaki Joe *rushes in. He is wearing motor bike leathers and a helmet.*

Joe Mr Ali, the papers are here. Rodge-ah's just unloading them.

DG Three at a time, I bet!

Mr Ali Thanks, Joe. *(To the others)* I'll only be a moment, I have to sort out the returns.

Mr Ali *goes out. There is a pause as* ***Gareth*** *looks around nervously. He makes an attempt to say hello, but decides against it. Eventually,* ***Caf*** *speaks up.*

Caf Who are you?

Gareth Gareth.

They all burst out laughing.

DG *(Mimics)* Gareth. Garrrethththth.

Caf Listen to him!

Joe Don't he talk funny!

Caf Looks funny as well.

DG *(To Gareth)* What are you doing here?

Gareth I've come for the job. On the window. It said there was a vacancy.

Caf That's 'cos someone left. They didn't get on with us. Know what I mean?

Gareth Oh.

DG Where are you from?

Gareth Wales.

Joe Where's that?

Caf Dunno.

Joe Isn't it in Scotland?

DG Don't be stupid, Joe. It's in Wales. Wales is a country.

Joe Well, I didn't know.

DG That's because you're thick.

Caf Shut up DG. *(To Gareth)* What was your name again?

Gareth Gareth.

Sharon I think it's a nice name.

Caf What?

Joe Eeeaaaarr!

Caf *(To Sharon)* Shut up, Guts! Anyway, it's too long. We'll call him Gaz.

Gareth No, it's Gareth, not Gaz.

Caf God, just listen to him. *(Mimics)* 'It's Garrreeethththth!' What a la di da!

DG More of a Yakki Da!

The others laugh.

Caf Yakki Da! I like it!

__Mr Ali__ returns.

Mr Ali Right, that's done. Have you introduced yourselves?

Caf Yeah. Haven't we, Yakki?

The kids giggle to themselves.

Mr Ali What do you mean . . . Yakki?

Caf Nothing.

Mr Ali I really don't understand you sometimes. This is Gareth. He's taking over Theresa's round while she's ill.

Caf That's not fair. Terry's round is dead easy.

DG Yeah.

Joe That's right.

Mr Ali I don't want any arguments or silliness. Gareth is doing Theresa's round and I'll see how he gets on with it.

The kids mutter among themselves. __Gareth__ begins to get embarrassed.

Mr Ali This isn't the way to treat newcomers, is it? Shamir, get a bag for Gareth. Then come through, Gareth, I'll go over the round with you.

__Shammy__ fetches a bag.

Mr Ali And the rest of you, come on! The papers are here! And I want them out on time, please.

__Mr Ali__ exits as the others begin to move. __Shammy__ goes to hand Gareth the bag but __DG__ stops him. __DG__ gives Gareth a tatty and torn bag.

DG Here's a bag for you, Yakki.

Gareth But it's got holes in it.

DG Yeah. Well it's for the leaks, like you get in Wales!

The joke dawns on the others and they leave laughing. ***Gareth*** *looks at the bag and then follows Mr Ali into the shop.*

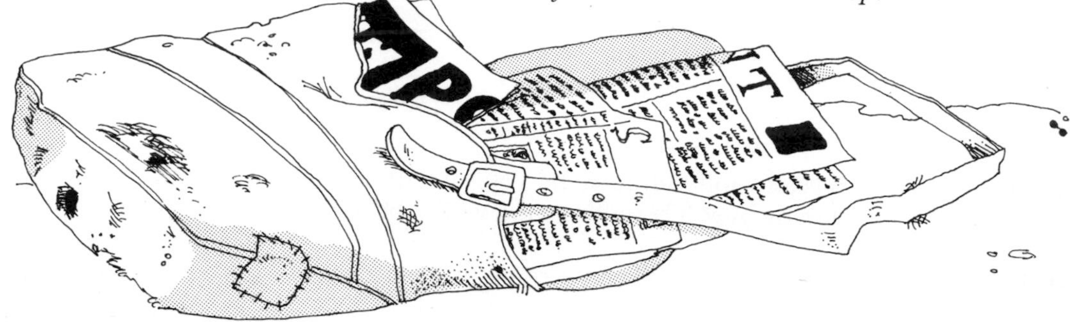

Scene 2

Later, in the back room of the shop. ***Mr Ali*** *is counting off the bags that have been returned.* ***Rodge-ah*** *enters. He takes his bag off and gives it to Mr Ali.*

Mr Ali Thank you.

Rodge-ah Goodnight, Mr Ali.

Mr Ali Goodnight. Oh, Roger?

Rodge-ah Yes?

Mr Ali Your round is next to Theresa's. Did you see Gareth? He should have finished a long time ago.

Rodge-ah Actually, I saw him hanging around outside.

Mr Ali Outside?

Rodge-ah Yes. He was standing there. I don't know why.

Mr Ali All right. Thank you, Roger. See you tomorrow.

Rodge-ah Yes. Bye.

***Rodge-ah** goes. **Mr Ali** shrugs and returns to checking the bags. **Gareth** enters the room.*

Mr Ali Ah, Gareth. Everything all right?

Gareth *(Shrugs)* Not bad.

Mr Ali You didn't get lost then?

Gareth No, it was easy.

Mr Ali Good. Would you like the job then?

Gareth S'pose so.

Mr Ali S'pose so? I thought you wanted the job pretty badly. You were keen enough earlier on this afternoon.

Gareth *(Snaps)* Well, I said I'd take it, didn't I?

He realizes he is being rude and shuts up.

Mr Ali Why didn't you want to see the others?

Gareth Eh?

Mr Ali You hung around outside until everyone had gone. There must be a reason.

Gareth It doesn't matter.

Mr Ali *(Firmly)* Nonsense. Suppose you stop sulking for a minute and tell me what's the matter.

Gareth *(After a pause)* It's all that lot.

Mr Ali What have they been up to?

Gareth Laughing at me. Making jokes about leeks.

Mr Ali Curry.

Gareth What?

Mr Ali With me it was curry. They made jokes about curry. I don't even like curry!

Gareth I don't like leeks.

They both smile.

Mr Ali So Catherine has been up to her old tricks again, has she?

Gareth Yes. And the other one, the leery one with the glasses. DG. Why's he called DG?

Mr Ali It's short for 'Double Glazing'. It's a nickname. A joke. Not a very nice one though.

Gareth Well, they were taking it out on my name and my accent.

Mr Ali You shouldn't let things like that bother you.

Gareth It's all right for you. You don't know what it's like.

Mr Ali Oh I do, Gareth. When I first came here, I had people saying all sorts of things about me. 'Oh, we'll be getting our papers delivered by elephant will we, Mr Ali?' and many other such things. Until they know and accept you, people are wary. It takes time to be accepted. You must let people get used to you before you can expect them to be friends.

Gareth I don't want to be friends with that lot. I've got friends in Wales. I didn't want to come to this dump anyway, but Dad couldn't get any work on the farms.

Mr Ali So you moved?

Gareth Yeah, he got a job here. In a warehouse. It isn't fair.

Mr Ali My parents came here over thirty years ago. They were among the first people from Pakistan to come to England. It was very hard for them. They didn't speak English very well, you see. My father had a job. Eventually he made friends, but it took a long time. My mother was terrified at going out of the door. She used to make my father do the shopping. She used to tell me that for the whole of her first year in England, she never left the house. For me things were easier.

Gareth *(A bit jealous)* But you get on all right with them all. They don't take it out on you.

Mr Ali *(Laughs)* Not now, no. When I first bought the shop, though, it was all rather different.

Gareth How d'you mean?

Mr Ali Well, before I came, the shop was owned by a Mrs Green . . .

. . . .

Scene 3

Inside the back of the shop. ***Caf***, ***DG***, ***Tealeaf***, ***Kawasaki Joe***, ***Shammy***, ***Sharon***, ***Bazzer***, ***Rodge-ah*** *are all sitting about chattering among themselves.*

Caf What's Mrs Green keeping us behind for?

Bazzer Dunno.

DG She said she'd got a surprise for us.

Caf Maybe she's giving us a rise.

Tealeaf I doubt it. She's a real stinge.

Bazzer I heard her talking to someone on the phone.

Caf Who to?

Bazzer The talking clock. *(He laughs. No one else does.)*

Caf That's not funny, Bazzer. You're never funny.

Bazzer Sorry.

DG Must be important for her to keep us all behind.

Rodge-ah Well, I can't stay for too long. I've got a lesson to go to.

DG What, going to your elocution lesson are you?

Shammy What's elly-thingy?

DG Learning to talk proper.

Caf You mean he pays someone to teach him to talk like that? I thought he must have fallen on his head when he was a baby!

The others laugh.

Rodge-ah Actually, it's a dancing lesson, if you must know.

DG Dancing lessons! What a wimp! Rodge-ah the wimp!

The others all burst out laughing.

Rodge-ah You're just jealous.

They burst out laughing again.
Mrs Green *comes in with* ***Mr Ali****. It immediately goes silent. Then the kids begin to whisper among themselves.*

Caf Who's he?

DG Dunno.

Tealeaf What's he want?

Caf If you shut up we'll find out.

Mrs Green Now then, is everyone here? Where's Theresa?

DG She's out collecting. Home for distressed donkeys or something.

Mrs Green Just like Theresa. Well, thank you for staying behind. I'd like to introduce you to Mr Ali.

Mr Ali Hello.

There are one or two grunts from the kids.

Mrs Green As you know, I'm not getting any younger and the strain of running a shop is getting worse. I can't cope with the early mornings any more, so I've decided to sell the shop.

Caf What!

Shammy You can't.

Tealeaf Sell it?

DG What about our jobs?

Caf Yeah! You can't sell it!

Mrs Green Yes, I've decided. Don't worry about your jobs. Mr Ali here has made me a very good offer for it *(she smiles at Mr Ali)* so you'll be working for him next month.

Caf *(Under her breath)* I'm not working for him.

Mrs Green So, I thought I'd better tell you and introduce you. Well, Mr Ali, here they are; my paperkids. What do you think?

Mr Ali They look a fine lot. Hello to you all. I must say, I'm looking forward to working here.

Caf *(Whispering to the others)* I'm not.

Mr Ali So, I'm Mr Ali. *(He looks round for someone to start introducing themselves – no one does.)*

***Mr Ali** turns to Caf.*

Mr Ali And you are?

Caf Very well, thank you.

Mr Ali Your name, I meant.

Caf *(Reluctantly)* Caf.

Mr Ali Caf?

Caf *(As though talking to a baby)* Short for Caferine.

Mr Ali Ahh.

Caf I'm the leader.

Mr Ali Oh! Were you elected?

Caf Nah! It's just that if anyone disagrees with me, I bash 'em.

Mr Ali I see. The lads as well?

Caf *(Menacingly)* Especially the lads.

The lads shuffle their feet. ***Mr Ali*** *smiles at Caf uncertainly and turns to Tealeaf.*

Mr Ali Hello. What's your name?

Tealeaf Tealeaf.

Mr Ali That's a strange name.

Tealeaf It's slang. Rhyming slang.

Mr Ali Oh!

Tealeaf Stands for thief. Tealeaf – thief.

Mr Ali *(Warily)* And why are you called that?

Tealeaf 'Cos I nick from shops.

Mr Ali I hope that you're not going to steal from this shop.

Tealeaf *just stares back.*

Mrs Green Yes, well, children, the rest of you can introduce yourselves later. Come on, Mr Ali, I'll make us a cup of tea. Thank you everyone. See you tomorrow.

Mrs Green *and* ***Mr Ali*** *go.*

Caf Well, I'm not working for him.

Bazzer Bet he'll turn it into a curry house. We'll have to deliver poppadoms.

DG Shut up, Bazzer, don't be stupid.

Caf I'm not working for him.

Tealeaf Why does she have to sell?

Bazzer Let's organise a protest march. Get Terry to organise it. She'll know what to do.

DG What good is that going to do?

Rodge-ah My parents think that there should be stricter immigration laws.

Caf What are you on about?

Rodge-ah Immigration laws.

Caf Shut up, you wimp.

Tealeaf I bet the place'll start to stink of curry.

Caf Yeah, they all stink of curry.

Shammy Hey, shut up. I don't. You're talking about me.

DG No we're not. You're different, Shammy.

Caf Yeah. You're not like him.

Shammy Well, what's the difference, then? You're just saying things without thinking about them. 'They all stink.' That's stupid.

There is an uneasy silence as ***Shammy*** *looks around.*

Shammy Do I smell of curry? *(To Caf)* Come on, smell my breath. Does that smell of curry?

Caf *looks embarrassed as* ***Shammy*** *stands in front of her.*

Caf *(Flustered)* No, but . . . but we *know* you. You're different. You're not like him. You're a mate. He looks . . . well . . . you know. He's got shifty eyes . . . I bet he's up to no good.

Shammy *(Sarcastically)* Oh, he *looks* different now. You make me sick, Caf! You really are stupid!

Shammy *marches out of the back room. There is an uneasy pause as the kids realize that Caf has been successfully challenged. They all look at each other before* ***Bazzer*** *breaks the silence.*

Bazzer We could go on strike.

DG Shut up, Bazzer. If we go on strike, we won't get any money.

Caf Well, I'm not working for him.

Joe I am. I need the money. I'm saving up for a motorbike. I've got to have a job.

Tealeaf And I'm still paying off my fines. I need a job.

Caf Well, I don't care about you lot. I'm not working for him.

Sharon I thought he looked nice.

DG Shut up, Guts.

Enter ***Mrs Green****.*

Mrs Green Oh, you're all still here. Thank you for staying tonight. Mr Ali's a lovely man. I'm sure you'll all get on very well with him.

Caf *(To the others quietly)* I'm sure we won't.

• •

Scene 4

The back room. ***Mr Ali*** *is checking bags and stock. Enter* ***Bazzer, Caf, Tealeaf*** *and* ***Sharon****.* ***Mr Ali*** *looks a bit shocked.*

Mr Ali Oh. You've finished early.

Tealeaf That's 'cos we're good.

Bazzer Yeah. Very good.

Caf *just stares at Mr Ali.*

Mr Ali I didn't think you'd be back so quickly. *(Pause)* I was just tidying some things up.

The kids start talking to each other.

Tealeaf See that film last night?

Caf No, I watched the curry advert instead.

Bazzer *giggles.*

Are you selling curry and poppadoms yet, Mr Ali?

Mr Ali Actually, Catherine, I don't like curry. I never eat it myself. Do you think we should start to sell it?

Caf *(To the others)* I'm not bothered.

Tealeaf I wouldn't nick any curry. Might nick poppadoms though.

Bazzer *giggles again.*
The shop bell rings.

Mr Ali Ah, a customer. Just put your bags down in the corner. I'll see you all tomorrow. Cheerio.

Mr Ali *leaves.*

Caf If I didn't need the money, I wouldn't work for him.

They take off their bags. ***Tealeaf*** *goes over to the stock.*

Tealeaf Wonder if there's anything worth nicking?

Caf Probably only curry.

Bazzer You're not going to nick anything, are you?

Tealeaf Dunno. Why not?

Bazzer He'd know it was us.

Tealeaf What a chicken! Let's see what there is.

DG *comes in and puts his bag down.*

Tealeaf Where's Ali gone?

DG In the shop.

Tealeaf Many in?

DG A few.

Tealeaf Good.

Sharon *(Quietly furious)* Why can't you leave things alone, Pauline?

Tealeaf Tealeaf to you, Guts.

Sharon My name's Sharon, not Guts.

Tealeaf What's up with you?

Sharon You make me sick, that's what. All of you. You too, Caf.

Caf *(Clenching her fists)* Oh, I do, do I?

Sharon Go on then, hit me. You're just a bully.

Caf What's wrong with you?

Sharon It's not fair! You're not giving him a chance. Like that kid last month. You took it out of him 'cos he talked funny.

Caf That wimp with a lithp?

DG I thay, did Thimon have a lithp? I didn't notith.

Sharon Yes, just like that.

Caf It was only a bit of fun.

Sharon He wasn't laughing.

Caf If he couldn't take a joke that was his bad luck.

Sharon Well you're doing it again. Stupid jokes. Why don't you give him a chance?

Caf Who? Ali?

Sharon Yes.

Caf Shut up, Guts.

Sharon Just because he's another colour, you think that there must be something wrong with him. What about Shammy, hey? What's different? Nothing. Well, I think that Mr Ali's all right.

Caf You would! My mum says . . .

Sharon Your mum says! Can't you think for yourself?

Caf Shut it, Guts! You're gonna get a belt in a minute.

__Tealeaf__ has been rummaging about on the shelves. She has found some packets. She turns to the others.

Tealeaf Here, what d'you reckon this is?

__DG__ and __Caf__ go to look. __Sharon__ stays where she is.

Tealeaf This white powder here, in poly bags. Hasn't got a label on. Do you reckon it might be worth nicking?

Caf Dunno. Might be sherbet.

Bazzer That's not sherbet.

Caf How d'you know?

Bazzer There's no liquorice with it.

Caf God, Bazzer, if you had a brain you'd be stupid.

DG I've seen something like this before . . .

Tealeaf There's a whole box of it here. Loads of bags. I wonder what it is?

Caf Taste it.

Tealeaf What?

Caf Open a packet and taste it.

Tealeaf Might be something horrible. You taste it.

Caf Now who's chicken? All right, I'll . . .

She is about to open the packet. __DG__ stops her.

DG No! Stop! Don't open it! Put it back!

__DG__ picks up the packet as though it were a tarantula spider.

Caf Have you gone bonkers!

DG I've just remembered where I've seen packets like this before. On telly . . . that programme about the Customs. They caught a bloke smuggling coke into the country. It was hidden in the spare wheel of his car, in bags just like this.

Bazzer You can't get done for smuggling Coca-Cola.

DG Not that coke, thicko!

Bazzer What then, the sort you put in boilers? That's black. Anyway, it's not a powder . . .

DG Shut up, you divvy. Not that sort. *(He beckons them to come closer.)* Coke. Cocaine. *(They stare)* Heroin. *(He whispers)* Drugs.

Tealeaf *(Shouts)* Drugs!

DG Shhh! He'll hear you. He's probably in a gang. We'll get our throats cut if they find out we've seen this.

Tealeaf Ooer!

Bazzer *(To Caf)* You could have got addicted. A boy at school told me. One taste and that's it.

Caf You sure?

Bazzer Yeah, honest!

Tealeaf Ooer! What we gonna do?

DG Get the others, have a meeting and then decide.

Caf Oi! DG . . . who gives the orders round here, me or you?

DG Sorry, Caf. What do you want to do?

Caf Well, I . . . er . . . get the others, have a meeting, and then decide.

Sharon You're all mad! Decide what?

Caf What to do about Ali!

Sharon Why?

Caf *(Shaking a packet at Sharon)* 'Cos he's got drugs in our papershop!

Sharon How d'you know it's drugs?

DG Drugs come from Pakistan. It was on the telly. The bloke they caught got the drugs from Pakistan.

Sharon *(Sarcastically)* So everyone from Pakistan is a drugs dealer? You lot are so stupid! I give up! I'm going home.

Caf You're comin' to the meeting!

Sharon Get knotted!

***Sharon** goes. **Caf** goes after her to pull her back but she sees Mr Ali coming towards the door. She turns to the others.*

Caf Ali's comin'! Put the stuff back!

*They scramble the packets back into the box, and put the box back onto the shelf. They all stand around looking suspicious. **Mr Ali** enters.*

Mr Ali What are you three up to?

Caf Nothing.

Tealeaf Nothing.

Bazzer Nothing.

Mr Ali Haven't you got homes to go to?

Caf Oh yeah. Come on, let's go.

*They run out leaving **Mr Ali** looking puzzled. He shrugs and checks the stock, looking at the polythene bags.*

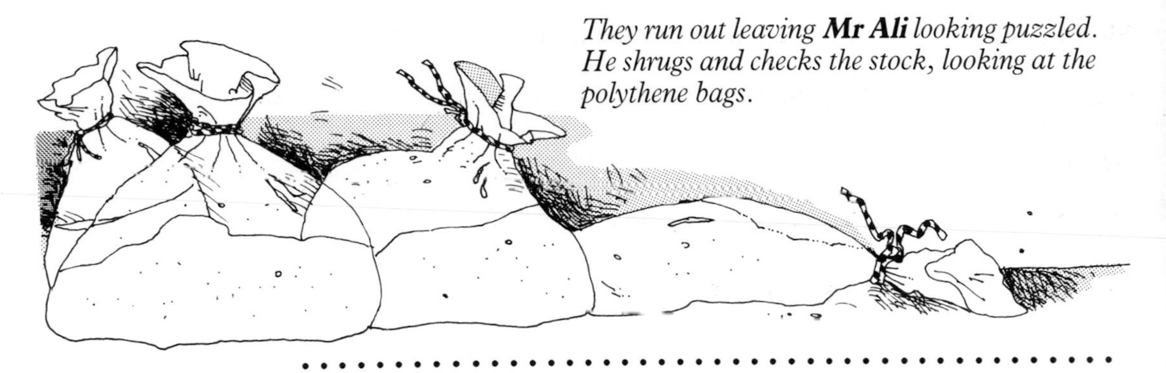

Scene 5

***Caf, Bazzer, Tealeaf, Shammy, Rodge-ah, DG** and **Kawasaki Joe** are sitting on and around a park bench.*

Caf So that's what we saw. Drugs. He's a dealer.

Shammy How can you be sure?

Caf I know. That's how.

Bazzer Yeah. It was like on the telly . . . white powder. I even tasted some.

Tealeaf You liar! You were scared! You didn't taste any at all.

Bazzer Well, I would have but he came back.

Tealeaf Dream on.

Caf Shut up arguing.

Shammy I bet it wasn't drugs.

Rodge-ah I think we should inform the appropriate authorities.

Caf What?

Rodge-ah Inform the appropriate authorities.

Tealeaf You swallowed a dictionary or something?

Rodge-ah No, I just think that . . .

Caf Shut up, wimpo. We've got to tell the police.

Rodge-ah *(Quietly)* That's what I said.

Bazzer Yeah. Then we'll be dead famous: we'll get in the papers and maybe on the telly.

Joe Yeah, great idea!

DG Hang on. If we tell the police, what are they going to do?

Tealeaf Arrest him.

Caf Then we'll be rid of him. We won't have to work for him no more.

DG But if he's a dealer, there must be others.

Caf So . . .?

DG He's just one . . . Don't you see?

Caf No.

DG There's more than one. He must be in a gang. If the police arrest him they might scare off the rest.

Bazzer I get it. Like on Top Cop. The detective followed a dealer and found out about some others. Mind you, he got into trouble. His partner had to come and rescue him, but that . . .

Caf Shut up, Bazzer. We're not on the telly.

DG No, but we could watch Ali. Maybe catch his gang.

Rodge-ah Won't that be dangerous?

Caf You scared?

Rodge-ah No, it's just that it could be dangerous.

Bazzer That's what happened in Top Cop. The detective got hurt and . . .

Caf Bazzer, *you'll* get hurt in a minute if you don't shut up.

DG If we caught all the gang, we'd probably get a big reward.

Caf You reckon?

DG Yeah. You always get rewards.

Tealeaf How much?

DG Dunno, but the more we catch, the more we'll get.

Caf Right then. That's it. We'll watch Ali and see who he sees.

Shammy How are you going to do that? You're at school during the day.

DG We'll organize a rota – each of us skive off a lesson.

Rodge-ah I'm not sure my mother will let me miss a lesson.

Caf You don't tell her then, stupid.

DG Right, let's start planning it out. Anyone got any ideas for spying on Ali?

They go into a huddle.

DIY Section

(See the explanation on page 4.)

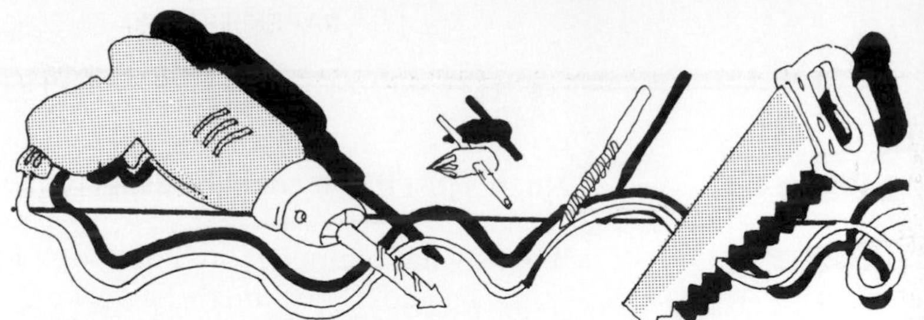

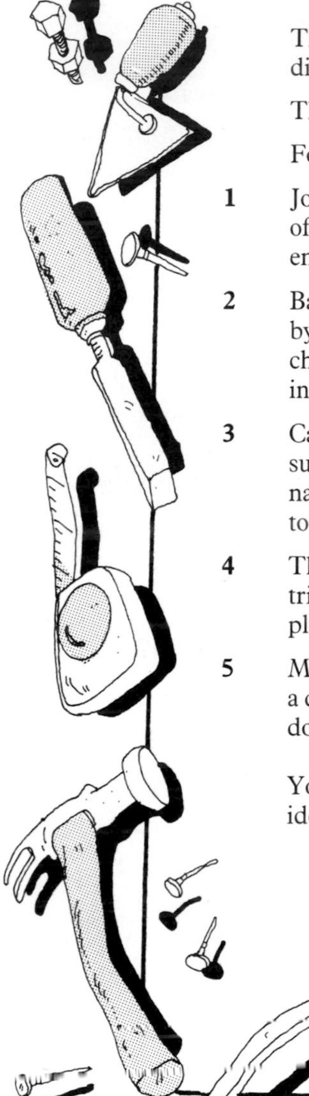

The kids have decided to start spying on Mr Ali, to see who he meets and discover whether he really is dealing in drugs.

Think of some of the situations that this could lead them into!

For instance:

1 Joe decides to watch from inside a dustbin. A woman comes out with a bucket of rubbish. She is talking to a neighbour and doesn't look inside the bin, so she empties the rubbish all over Joe.

2 Bazzer hides himself in a big cardboard box inside the shop. (It can walk in all by itself while Mr Ali isn't looking, if Bazzer has cut the bottom out of it, and changes places every time Mr Ali's back is turned.) Some delivery people come in with a trolley, load the box onto a van, and drive away.

3 Caf and DG hide behind a car watching the shop. The car drives away suddenly, and they are left bent double. Mr Ali gapes at them. They try to look natural (by impersonating Groucho Marx or doing a dance, or by pretending to look for something on the ground).

4 The kids 'shadow' Mr Ali when he goes out. They all wear trench coats and trilby hats (as near as they can manage). They turn up in the most unlikely places. Mr Ali gets very confused by it all.

5 Mr Ali comes into the shop. Rodge-ah is examining the counter. He is wearing a deerstalker hat and carrying a magnifying glass like Sherlock Holmes. How does he explain this to Mr Ali?

You can try some or all of these ideas out, but don't be afraid to use *your own* ideas.

Scene 6

Back of the shop. Enter ***Caf, Tealeaf, Bazzer, Joe*** *and* ***DG****.*

Caf So no one has found anything out yet?

Tealeaf No.

Bazzer It takes ages. On Top Cop, the detective had to wait ages, months and months.

Caf Don't be stupid, Bazzer. We can't wait that long.

Bazzer But no one's seen *anything* yet. What are we going to do?

Caf We'll have to wait. Sshhh, it's him.

Joe What's he doing? Is he coming in here?

Caf (*Looking into the shop*) No, he's got someone with him. He's got a fur coat on.

Tealeaf Who, Ali?

Caf No, the other one. He's smokin' a cigar. Hey – he's giving something to Ali! It's money . . .

DG Let's see. Cor, look at that . . . Loadsamoney!

Tealeaf How much?

Caf How do I know? There's a pile of fivers.

DG It's a pay off!

The others look at him.

This is what we've been waiting for! The other bloke must be the banker. He's payrolling the operation.

Joe What are you on about?

DG Look, dodo, the bloke in the fur coat gives Ali the money to smuggle in the drugs.

Caf So that's what the money's for!

DG Yep. *(Being clever)* It's probably being laundered.

Tealeaf You what? You mean they wash it?

DG Well, not exactly . . .

Tealeaf You can't wash money. I left a fiver in my jeans once and my mum washed 'em and it came out lookin' like used bog roll.

DG Look, you don't wash money when you launder it.

Joe What do you do then?

DG *(Who doesn't really know)* Never mind, it's just what they do. Perhaps they pass it from one to the other in a laundry . . .

Joe This is a papershop.

DG Well, perhaps the laundry's closed . . . look, never mind that, Ali's being paid off, right? Now I reckon the next thing he'll do is to take the stuff round to his pushers.

Joe His what?

Caf Don't think about it, Joe, you'll only get brain-ache. Hey, watch out! He's said goodbye to the other one, he's comin' in here.

They scatter and try to look innocent. ***Mr Ali*** *comes in.*

Mr Ali You're all early tonight. The papers aren't due for half an hour.

Caf We thought that we'd . . . er . . . we'd . . . er . . . get here early!

Mr Ali Oh, well as you're here, perhaps you could do me a favour.

Mr Ali *takes one of the boxes full of polythene bags from the shelf and holds it out to Caf. She shrinks away as if he'd tried to hand her a live grenade.*

Mr Ali Would you take this, and . . . is something wrong, Catherine?

Caf What? Er, yeah, er . . . a bad back. Yeah. I've got a bad back.

Mr Ali You're young to have a bad back.

DG Well it's a new thing, it only affects the under sixteens. It's infectious as well.

Mr Ali Bad backs? Infectious?

DG Yeah. I think I've caught it as well. Aaaaaghhh! *(He holds his back.)* Anyway, what's in the boxes, Mr Ali?

Mr Ali That doesn't concern you, especially as your 'infectious bad back' is stopping you from helping me move them.

Tealeaf Why are you moving them, Mr Ali?

Mr Ali Because I need to get rid of them.

Tealeaf Why?

Mr Ali Because I'm not supposed to have them. I could be in serious trouble if they were found in the shop. Are you going to help, or not?

Tealeaf Er, yeah, okay.

Joe Yeah.

Bazzer All right.

Mr Ali Thank you. I'll go and unlock my car.

Mr Ali *goes out.*

Tealeaf Hear that? 'Could be in serious trouble if it was found in the shop'!

Bazzer He's admitted it! Time to call in the law. Time for Dirty Harry to load up his Magnum 45 and KERPOW! *(He mimes shooting a gun, American cop style.)*

Caf Bazzer, you're mental. This is serious. You and me are going to call the police. DG, get the others here quick. Joe, Tealeaf, you stay here. Keep Ali talking.

Tealeaf What?

Joe What about?

Caf Anything. The weather. The price of ice lollies.

Joe Eh?

Caf Just keep him talking, right?

__Bazzer__ and __Caf__ rush out, followed by __DG.__
__Joe__ and __Tealeaf__ are flustered.
__Mr Ali__ enters.

Mr Ali Where are the others?

Joe Oh, they . . . er . . . just nipped out.

Mr Ali I see.

Pause. __Mr Ali__ moves to pick up the box.

Joe Nice weather, isn't it?

Mr Ali *(Surprised)* But it's raining, Joe.

Joe Oh yeah. I mean for ducks. Ha ha!

Mr Ali I suppose so.

Joe It was nice yesterday, though.

Mr Ali Yes, it was. No it wasn't. It rained yesterday as well.

Pause. __Joe__ and __Tealeaf__ exchange desperate glances.

Tealeaf I bet you've met my uncle.

Mr Ali Pardon?

Tealeaf I bet you've met my uncle. He went to Pakistan about five years ago on business. You probably met him.

Mr Ali Pauline, there are millions of people in Pakistan.

Tealeaf Oh.

Mr Ali Besides, I've never been to Pakistan. I was born in Birmingham.

Tealeaf Well, he's been to Birmingham as well. Shopping. You probably bumped into him in Birmingham.

Mr Ali Pauline, are you all right?

Tealeaf Yes. Oh yes. Perfect.

***Tealeaf** looks desperately at Joe.*

Joe We're having curry tonight. Dad's making it. All those spices . . . dead hot. I love curry. Do you?

Mr Ali You know I don't. I prefer fish and chips. Are you sure you're both okay?

Joe *(With exaggeration)* Yes. Honest.

Tealeaf *(Suddenly)* Look! A mouse!

Mr Ali What?

Tealeaf *(Points)* A mouse there. Just running across the floor.

Mr Ali Where?

Tealeaf Oh, it's gone.

Mr Ali Are you sure it was a mouse?

Tealeaf Yeah, dead sure. It was a white one.

Mr Ali I'll have to get a trap down.

Tealeaf It was a white one. Do you get white mice in Pakistan?

Mr Ali I don't know, Pauline, I've never been there.

Tealeaf Oh yeah, right. Do you get them in Birmingham?

__Mr Ali__ slaps his head in amazement.

Mr Ali Yes, I'm sure they do. Now I must move these bags . . .

__Caf__ and __Bazzer__ rush in.

Tealeaf You took your time.

Caf Time? Er yeah, nearly four-thirty. Hello, Mr Ali.

__DG__ and __Rodge-ah__ rush in. __Sharon__ and __Shammy__ follow them.

DG Hello, Mr Ali.

Rodge-ah Hello, Mr Ali.

Mr Ali Are you all right?

DG We heard a police siren.

The kids smile to each other.

Caf *(Exaggerating)* A police car? I *wonder* what's going on? Gosh, it sounds as though it's stopping.

__Mr Ali__ looks confused.
Enter two __Police Officers__.

Police 1 Excuse me, sir. Mr Ali, is it?

Mr Ali Yes.

Police 1 Sorry to bother you, sir, only we've received some information.

From some youngsters. *(Looks at the kids who all look skywards and whistle.)* It's probably a false alarm but we have to follow these things up . . .

Caf It's him! It's him! Arrest him! I was the one who rang. Do I get the reward?

Bazzer I rang as well.

Caf *hits* ***Bazzer.***

Caf Shut up! Do I get the money?

Police 1 Now then, young lady, calm down.

Mr Ali Officer, what's this all about?

Police 1 As I said, probably nothing, sir, but we've had a report that you have in this shop certain substances of a forbidden nature.

Mr Ali Oh dear. I had hoped that no one would find out.

Police 1 Oh, had you? *(**Police 1**'s attitude changes)* Do you admit to having these substances?

Mr Ali Well, yes, but . . .

Police 1 Well then, sunshine, that puts a different complexion on the matter. Would you mind telling me where to find this stuff?

Mr Ali Where to find it?

Police 1 Otherwise we'll have to send for the dog.

Mr Ali The dog?

Police 1 Sniffer dog. You do realize the seriousness of this offence, don't you, sonny Jim?

Mr Ali Well, surely it's not as serious as all that . . .

Police 1 Not serious? Not serious? Well, I'd like to hear your idea of what *is* serious, chummy.

Mr Ali But I thought a small fine . . .

Police 1 Small fine? Listen at him. He's as good as the telly! By the time we've finished with you, matey, you'll be looking at the wrong end of ten years inside.

Mr Ali What!!

Police 1 At least ten years, could be nearer fifteen.

Mr Ali But . . .

Police 1 Now come on, sunbeam, come on, no more stalling, where is it?

Bazzer Over there, in them boxes. They're full of poly bags, just like in Miami Vice.

Police 1 All right, lad, leave this to me.

Mr Ali But . . .

Police 1 Now you just shut up. You're in enough trouble. All right, Constable, open the bag.

***Police 2** opens the box, takes out a bag and opens it very slowly, hesitates, then slowly and carefully, wets a finger and dips it in the bag, sniffs it, then tastes it. **Police 2** looks puzzled. Wets finger again, dips it in again and tastes it again.*

Police 1 *(In a hushed whisper)* Well, Constable? What is it?

Police 2 Hard to say, Sarge. Could be Birds, could be Nestlés.

Police 1 What?

Police 2 It's custard powder, Sarge.

Mr Ali Of course it is. What did you think it was?

During the next few lines, the kids start to slip off: ***DG*** *first, then* ***Shammy, Rodge-ah, Sharon*** *and* ***Joe****. Only* ***Caf, Bazzer*** *and* ***Tealeaf*** *are left.*

Police 1 *(Becoming very polite again)* Ah, well, like I said, sir, we got this report concerning drugs . . .

Mr Ali Drugs? You thought I was keeping drugs?

Police 1 Er, well . . . sir . . .

Mr Ali *(Laughs)* Good heavens, officer, how ridiculous!

Police 1 But you admitted . . .

Mr Ali Oh dear, I'll have to tell you all about it. You see, Mrs Green, who used to own the shop, used to get supplies from . . . er . . . somewhere she shouldn't. I think someone from a hotel used to pass things on to her and she sold them to her customers cheaply. A bit of a 'fiddle', I think. I found these bags of custard powder and realized what she had been doing, so I was going to get rid of them.

Caf But you told us you'd be in serious trouble if they was found!

Bazzer Yeah! That's right!

Mr Ali I didn't want to be involved in the 'fiddle'. It would have made me an 'accessory', wouldn't it, officer?

Police 1 Well, I suppose . . .

Mr Ali Besides, I didn't want to get Mrs Green into trouble. She's a lovely old lady.

Caf Well, what about that drugs dealer who was in the shop just now?

Mr Ali 'Drugs dealer'? That 'drugs dealer' was my uncle, Catherine. He's helping me to buy the shop. He was giving me money to buy new stock.

Police 1 I see, sir. Right, young lady, over here.

Caf It wasn't me, honest. It was him. *(She points at Bazzer.)*

Bazzer You liar! It was you!

***Caf** hits him.*

Caf Shut up!

Police 1 Okay, sir. We'll sort this out.

Mr Ali You won't prosecute, will you?

Police 1 No, sir. We'll just have a little chat, about wasting our time.

Mr Ali *(Chuckles)* Paper Tigers.

Police 1 Sir?

Mr Ali Paper Tigers, officer. They're my Paper Tigers.

Police 1 I don't follow, sir.

Mr Ali I'll explain some time.

Police 1 *(Puzzled)* Yes, sir. Right, you three. Tigers need to go behind bars. Down to the station with you. Come on.

***Caf, Bazzer** and **Tealeaf** are led away, protesting.*

....

Scene 7

*The back room. We are now in the present, with **Mr Ali** and **Gareth**.*

Mr Ali So, there you are, Gareth. They were ready to believe the worst of me, because I was different. People are like that, I'm afraid. Anyway, you see that I know exactly what you are feeling.

Gareth What happened to Caf?

Mr Ali They let her off with a warning about wasting police time. I thought it was funny – I let her keep her job, it seemed only fair. Funny thing, after that the rest of the group seemed to change towards me. I'm not certain why. Maybe it was the pay rise I gave them! They liked the name Paper Tigers as well. That's what they call themselves now. I think it suits them.

Gareth It's a good name. What does it mean?

Mr Ali Whatever you want it to mean. So, Gareth, do you want the job?

Gareth Yes, please.

Mr Ali Good. Well, it's yours. Start properly tomorrow. Six-thirty. Okay?

Gareth Okay.

***Gareth** starts to go.*

Mr Ali Remember, things take time. You have to get to know people and let them get to know you.

Gareth Yes, I suppose so. Thanks.

Mr Ali My pleasure. Goodnight, Gareth.

Gareth Goodnight.

. . . .

Scene 8

*The paper shop. **Mr Ali, Caf, DG** and **Tealeaf** are getting papers ready. The kids start to leave just as **Gareth** walks in.*

Caf It's Yakki Da!

DG *(Sarcastically)* Hello, Yakki. Garrrrrrreth.

Caf, DG *and* ***Tealeaf*** *leave, laughing.*

Mr Ali It takes time.

Gareth Yeah.

Mr Ali Well, all set then?

Gareth Yeah. No problems.

Kawasaki Joe *rushes in.*

Mr Ali You're early, Joe.

Joe Gotta fix my Vespa before I go to school. There's something wrong with it.

Mr Ali Oh dear, nothing serious, I hope.

Joe Dunno. It won't go. It conked out yesterday. The engine just cut out when I opened it up.

Gareth Could be the carburettor. You might have the mixture set wrong.

Joe What?

Gareth The carb. There's a screw that adjusts the fuel-air mix. Or it could be a blocked jet, or your needle valve.

Joe How do you know?

Gareth I used to have a bike. On the farm.

Joe What sort?

Gareth Scrambler. Kawasaki 50cc.

Joe God. You lucky devil. Was it good?

Gareth Brilliant. Used to do trials on it.

Joe I couldn't do that on my Vespa.

Gareth Do you want a hand fixing your bike?

Joe Do you mind?

Gareth No. I'd like to. Honest.

Joe Thanks, Yakki. Sorry, I mean Gareth.

Gareth Yakki.

Joe What?

Gareth Yakki. It's a good nickname. I like it.

Joe Oh, right.

Mr Ali Well you'd better get off then – it looks as though you've got a lot to do before you go to school.

Joe Yeah. Come on then. We'll do the rounds together. It'll be quicker.

Gareth Okay.

Joe Bye.

Gareth Bye, Mr Ali.

Mr Ali Cheerio, Joe, cheerio Gareth . . . or should I say Yakki?

Gareth *smiles.* ***Joe*** *and* ***Gareth*** *go to leave.* ***Caf*** *shouts from outside.*

Caf *(Nastily)* Oi, Joe, come on. Are you gonna stand talking to Curry Face all morning?

Joe *and* ***Gareth*** *leave.*

Mr Ali *(Frowns, then smiles sadly)* Oh yes, these things definitely take time.

Caf's Baf

The Characters

Caf	*the 'Paper Tigers'*
DG	
Shammy	
Sharon	
Kawasaki Joe	
Rodge-ah	
Bazzer	
Tealeaf	
Yakki-da	
Mr Ali	*
Police 1	*
Police 2	*
Mrs Perkes	*a customer*
Mrs Roberts	*owner of the 'Greasy Spoon' café*
Mr Cross	*a plumber*
Mr Ali's Mother	

* see **Paper Tigers**

Scene 1

The back room of the paper shop. ***DG, Sharon*** *and* ***Rodge-ah*** *are collecting their papers.*

DG (*To* ***Rodge-ah***) Oi, you, wimpo! You can do Lawley Crescent for me today. And you can do Everidge Avenue, Guts.

Rodge-ah Why should we?

DG 'Cos if you don't, I'll tell Caf what you've been doing.

Rodge-ah But we haven't done anything!

DG So what? I'll make something up. And then . . . well, you don't want to get on the wrong side of Caf, do you?

Sharon You're always making us do your round. I hate you!

DG So what? I don't care. Just get it done.

Sharon *and* ***Rodge-ah*** *go.* ***Caf*** *comes in as they go out. She is wearing a stereo walkman, jigging to the beat. She starts sorting papers.* ***DG*** *sniffs, then wrinkles his nose . . .*

DG Pheeuuu!

Caf *(Turning slowing and taking her headphones off)* You what?

DG There's an awful pong in here, can't you smell it?

Caf No.

DG Yeah, an 'orrible sort of fishy, cheesy pong, like the inside of a PE bag that hasn't been emptied for a week. Can't you smell it?

Caf No!

Tealeaf, Shammy *and* ***Yakki-da*** *enter.*

Tealeaf Hiya. Cor, what's that?

DG See, she can smell it too.

Shammy Smell what? Wooooerrrgh! It's just hit me! *(He starts to karate chop the air.)* Aaargh, it's got me! Help! *(Continues to hit the air)* That's evil, that is.

DG Caf can't smell nothing, she says.

Yakki Maybe she's got a cold. Got a cold, Caf?

Caf No!!

Tealeaf It smells like my dad's socks.

Shammy No, what it smells like is them giblets you get inside chickens in a little poly bag.

Yakki Yeah! My mum dropped one behind the fridge once and when we found it . . . *Yuk*!

DG I'll tell you what it smells like, you know when you open a packet of dry roast peanuts? That 'orrible smell? Just like that.

Yakki No, it's worse than that. It's like the squelchy cow pats we used to get on the farm in Wales. *(To Caf)* Are you sure you can't smell anything?

Caf No! I can't smell it and I've heard enough about it, okay?

***Joe** comes in.*

Joe Gorstreuth!! Has something died?

Caf *(To Joe, menacingly)* Not yet!

Joe That's the worst niff I've niffed in weeks.

***Caf** grabs hold of Joe's lapels and holds him nose to nose.*

Caf *(Very quietly)* Belt up. *(She lets Joe go)* Now listen to me, you comedians, 'cos I'm not going to say this again. I haven't had a baf in two weeks. Our baf is bust. Right? Now, I don't want to hear any more funny stuff about smells, niff, socks or cow pats. If anyone feels like laughing, they'll be doing it in hospital. Get it?

The others nod in agreement.

Caf In fact, the next person to mention pongs is going to get my fist right up the . . .

***Mr Ali** enters.*

Mr Ali Good morning. I . . .

He stops and sniffs. He wrinkles his nose in disgust.

Caf *(Menacingly)* You can't smell nothing, can you, Mr Ali?

The others hold their breath and wait. ***Mr Ali*** *doesn't know what's going on, but he does know when to agree with Caf.*

Mr Ali No, Catherine, not a thing.

Caf Good.

Mr Ali** shakes his head and exits. A confrontation has been avoided.* ***DG, Tealeaf, Shammy *and* ***Joe*** *sigh with relief.* ***Bazzer*** *bursts in.*

Bazzer Hiya! Did you see . . . POOOEURGHHHHH! WORASTINK!

Caf** attacks him.* ***Shammy, Joe *and* ***Tealeaf*** *try to hold her back.* ***DG*** *steps to the back and watches with enjoyment.*

Caf I'll kill him.

Shammy Watch it, Bazzer!

Tealeaf Gerroff him!

Joe Don't hurt him!

Yakki Grab her, quick!

Caf All right! Leggo.

Shammy Do you promise not to kill him?

Caf Can't I kill him just a little bit?

Shammy No.

Caf Okay, okay.

Bazzer *(Shocked)* What did I do?

Tealeaf You mentioned pongs.

Bazzer Yeah, well there's this terrible . . . *(**Caf** looks murder at him)* . . . Well now you mention it, I suppose it's quite a nice pong really, I've niffed worse . . .

Yakki I'd shut up if I were you, Bazzer.

Joe What I don't get is, how did you bust your bath?

Caf Well, it wasn't any good to start with, one of those cheapo plaggy bafs that bend when you sit in 'em. And it was old. My mam was hanging the washing up . . .

Joe In the bath?

Caf It was raining, thicko. So she was hanging it up on the string fing over the baf, only she forgot to take her stilettos off and that was it.

Bazzer *(Catching on)* So she put a hole in your bath and that's why you . . .

Caf glares.

. . . er, why you . . . *(changing the subject hurriedly, pointing at the walkman)* . . . Hey, that's sound!

Caf What? This? Yeah. *(Proud)* S'alright.

Tealeaf Hey, wicked! I've seen those in the shops. Dead expensive!

Caf I've saved up for it for ages.

Joe I could have one of them on my Vespa.

Caf You touch this and I'll wrap your Vespa round your neck.

Joe I only said *could*.

Caf I saved up for nearly a year to buy this, so none of you even looks at it, right?

The others quickly agree. ***Mr Ali*** *returns.*

Mr Ali Have you got your papers yet? Come on, your teachers will be complaining that your rounds have made you late for school again.

Yakki, Shammy, Bazzer *and* ***Joe*** *exit.* ***Caf*** *and* ***Tealeaf*** *are about to follow when* ***DG*** *stops them.*

DG *(Secretly)* Hey, you two, come here.

Caf Not now, we'll be late else.

DG Please yourselves then. I thought you might be interested in knowing where you could get a bath, that's all.

Caf A baf?! Where?

DG Not here. See you outside the chippy, after school.

DG *leaves with* ***Tealeaf.*** ***Caf*** *stands in thought.*

Mr Ali Catherine!

Caf *(Jumping)* Okay! *(Mutters)* Slave driver!

***Caf** leaves.*

. . . .

Scene 2

*A street corner outside the chip shop. **Caf** and **Tealeaf** are waiting for DG.*

Caf Where's DG? He'd better get here soon, or I'll do him.

Tealeaf You're in a right mood. What's up?

Caf Old Ratfaced Ratcliffe, that's what.

Tealeaf Who?

Caf Our games teacher. Don't you know anythin'?

Tealeaf We don't have her, we have potty Potter. She's a bit mad but she's all right though.

Caf Ratface isn't. She wouldn't let me have a shower.

Tealeaf What? I don't believe it! A games teacher who won't let you have a shower? Potter makes us have one even if we're not even sweating. Why wouldn't Ratcliffe let you have one?

Caf 'Cos I hadn't done games.

Tealeaf Oh, right. Well, why don't you do games? Then she'll let you have a shower.

Caf I never do games. On principle.

Tealeaf Yeah, but while your bath's bust . .

Caf You know what she said, the sarky dragon? *(Puts on a posh teacher's voice)* 'In any case, Catherine, I'm afraid at the moment you'd pollute the municipal water supply.'

Tealeaf What's the munipi-thingy?

Caf I dunno, I'm just telling you what she said.

DG *arrives.*

Tealeaf Here he is.

Caf About time. Where have you been?

DG Doing a spot of detecting.

Caf You what? We've been hanging about here, while you've been playing detectives?

Tealeaf He's not a detective, he's defective.

DG All right, if you're not interested.

Caf Come on then, where's the baf you were on about?

DG Sure you want to know?

Caf Course I do. Get on with it

DG No, I can tell you're not bothered.

Caf *(Grabbing DG)* Tell me, while you've still got teef!

DG Okay, okay! Listen, you know Ali?

Tealeaf Of course we do.

DG Yeah, but do you know he's bought a house?

Caf A house? I thought he lived in that flat over the shop.

DG He does!

Caf Then what's he want a house for?

DG Aha!

Caf What's 'Aha!' mean?

DG Well, why's he bought a house if he's got a flat?

Caf That's what I've just asked *you*!

DG So he can rent it out.

Tealeaf So?

DG I was reading about it in the paper, about these slum landlords. They buy up cheap houses, fill 'em full of homeless families and get hundreds of pounds a week from the Social Security.

Caf Really?

DG Yeah. It's awful, isn't it? 'Making fortunes out of misery'. That's what the papers said.

Tealeaf Well, so what?

DG So this is the interesting bit. This house was a right tip when Ali bought it, so he's had to spend a load of money on getting it put right. And guess what he had delivered yesterday?

Caf What?

DG A bath!

Caf So?

DG So, why don't you nick it?

Caf Nick it?

DG Yeah, nick it.

Tealeaf Hang on, how do you know all this about Ali and the house and the bath?

DG 'Cos the house he's bought is in the next street to ours. In fact I can see the back of it out of my bedroom window.

Tealeaf So you've seen the bath . . . how do we get it out? I know about

	nicking things and you can't nick a bath just like that.
Caf	Yeah, it'll have pipes and taps and stuff on it.
DG	It hasn't, though. The plumber hasn't been yet. The builders have smashed the old one up but the new one's not been fitted yet. I've just been talking to the trainee who works for the builder. He says the plumber's not coming till tomorrow.
Tealeaf	We could do it, Caf.
Caf	I don't like it. I don't nick fings.
DG	It's not really nicking, is it? You nick money and jewels and things. This is only a bath.
Caf	It's still nicking.
DG	Anyway, what's Ali going to do with the house? He's going to be a slum landlord and cheat people. That's a lot worse than nicking.
Caf	I dunno . . .
DG	What's up with you? You goin' soft or something?
Caf	You watch it!
DG	Well then, you joined the Ali fan club? I thought you'd want to have a go at him.
Caf	Weeeell . . .
DG	Just think of it as moving the bath from one place to another.
Caf	What do you reckon, Tealeaf? You're the expert.
Tealeaf	Let's do it.
Caf	It's got to be tonight.
Tealeaf	I can make it tonight.

DG I'm glad you've decided. I'll see you tomorrow then.

Caf Oi! Where do you think you're going?

DG Home. I've told you about the bath, haven't I?

Caf Yeah, but you're coming with us.

DG What, me? Nicking?

Caf It's not really nickin' though is it? You said.

DG Well, no, but . . .

Caf Right. We'll see you outside Ali's house at eight o'clock. It'll be dark by then. You can show us where it is now.

Tealeaf Cor, this is excitin', innit?

Caf Yeah. A baf for me mam and we'll get Ali back for the drugs. Come on, DG.

__Caf__ and __Tealeaf__ exit. __DG__ hesitates. He looks worried. Then he thinks of an idea and grins nastily. He runs after them.

. . . .

Scene 3

The bathroom at Mr Ali's new house. The bath is lying in the middle of the floor. We can't see __Caf__ and __Tealeaf__ but we can hear them whispering.

Tealeaf You sure this is it?

Caf It's where DG showed us. Anyway, it's the only empty house in the street.

Tealeaf Where is he anyway?

Caf He's late as usual. He'd better come, or I'll put him on crutches.

Pause.

Tealeaf Cooooor. Dark, innit?

Caf *(Sarcastically)* It usually is at night. At least we got in okay. Good job Ali left the back door open for the builders.

Tealeaf Which one d'you reckon is the bathroom?

Caf If it's like DG's house, it'll be the room at the end of the landing.

Tealeaf What, this door here?

Caf That's it. Now, we don't want any noise. Sssshhhh. Grab hold of the door handle. When I nod my head, turn it.

Pause. ***Caf*** *gives a muffled cry of pain.*

Caf Ow! Turn the door handle, *not* my *head*, you wally.

Tealeaf Oh yeah, right. Sorry.

Tealeaf *and* ***Caf*** *enter the bathroom. There is very little light.* ***Tealeaf*** *stops and then suddenly grabs Caf.*

Tealeaf Oooer!

Caf Wossup? Wossup!

Tealeaf *(Pointing a trembling finger)* It's here!

Caf Well, of course it's here. That's what we've come for, divvy.

Tealeaf Yeah, but it doesn't look like a bath. It looks like the mummy's tomb.

Caf Whose mummy?

Tealeaf Not anybody's mummy, an *Egyptian* mummy. Like in that TV programme, 'The Treasure of Tooting Common', or something like that.

Caf Are you all right?

Tealeaf Course I am. Listen, there's these pyramids and they put mummies in them.

Caf What for?

Tealeaf Well, you've got to put them somewhere, haven't you? And these priests put all these 'orrible curses on them and then when these explorers found them the curse got 'em and they all died.

Caf Really?

Tealeaf Yeah. Horrible, gruesome deaths . . .

There is a creaking noise.

Tealeaf Wossat?

Caf What?

Tealeaf That noise?

Caf What noise?

There is another creak.

Tealeaf *That* noise!

Caf I dunno . . . the wind?

Tealeaf The wind doesn't go 'creeeeaaak', it goes, 'whhoooooo', stupid.

Caf Who're you calling stupid?

There is a horrible spooky laugh.

Tealeaf Aaaaaghhh! Caf, it's the curse!

Caf The what?

Tealeaf The curse of Tooting Common! It's his ghost coming to get us.

Caf *(Nervously)* There's no such thing as ghosts.

There is another laugh.

Tealeaf I'm going to be sick! Caf, hold my hand.

Pause.

Tealeaf *(Quivering)* Caaaaaf . . .?

Caf What?

Tealeaf You're holding my left hand, aren't you?

Caf Yeah.

Tealeaf Then who's holding my *right* hand?

***Bazzer** has crept in and is sitting beside them. He turns a torch on under his face, to make it look really spooky and evil. He gives a spine chilling laugh.*

Bazzer WHOOAARRRRRHHH HAR HAR HAR!!!!

***Caf** and **Tealeaf** scream their heads off. **Bazzer** collapses with laughter. **Caf** is the first to recover.*

Caf Bazzer! You . . . You . . .

Bazzer *(In between screams of laughter)* You two . . . Your faces . . . hoo hoo hoo. . . .

Tealeaf God! My heart nearly stopped then.

Caf You hold him while I break something!

Bazzer Hoo hoo! Hold on, it was only a bit of fun!

Caf A bit of fun? A bit of fun? You nearly killed us! *And* you've made enough noise to wake up the dead!

Bazzer So what? There's a Hammer Horror film on BBC 1. Nobody's going to notice a few more screams.

Caf Ssssh!

They all listen.

Tealeaf I can't hear anything.

Caf *(To Bazzer)* Okay, thicko, what are you doing here?

Bazzer DG sent me. Said he couldn't come. He's washing his hair or something.

Caf I'll do him!

Bazzer Why? He sent me, didn't he?

Caf That's why!

Bazzer Oh well, if you don't want my help.

Caf Oi! Come here. Now you're here, you might as well give us a hand. We've got to get this baf onto the landing.

Bazzer Hey, did I tell you, I woke up this morning and there was a jumbo jet parked outside my bedroom.

Caf A jumbo jet?

Bazzer Yeah. I must have left the landing light on! *(He bursts into giggles.)*

Tealeaf Just ignore him, perhaps he'll go away.

Caf You're as bad. All that rubbish about Tooting Common.

Tealeaf It's not rubbish!

Bazzer She's right. I saw that programme as well and that bath does look a bit like a tomb.

Tealeaf *(To Caf)* See. And the squiggles on the wallpaper, they look like Egyptian hieroglyphics.

Bazzer Except the ones by the skirting board, they look like Egyptian *lower*oglyphics! *(He giggles)*

Caf You're both mental.

Tealeaf It's true about the mummy, Tooting Common. He was a king . . .

Bazzer He? Must have been a daddy then!

Caf Bazzer! Shut up!

Bazzer Some people have got no sense of humour . . .

Tealeaf Here, hang on, Caf. Even if we get the bath out, how are we going to get it to your house? It's miles away!

Caf We can carry it, can't we?

Tealeaf Have you tried lifting it? It weighs a ton!

Bazzer I've got an idea.

Caf *You've* got an idea?

Bazzer Yeah.

Caf I bet it's a rubbish one.

Bazzer No, listen. Joe's got an old pram, he's going to make it into a go-cart. We could wheel the bath on that.

Tealeaf That's a brilliant idea, Bazzer . . .

Bazzer *(Really pleased)* Thanks.

Tealeaf . . . considering what a complete idiot you are!

Bazzer Hey!

Caf Come on then, help us to get the baf downstairs then go to Joe's for the cart. After three, one . . . two . . . three . . . LIFT!

They lift the bath, but as they do so, they hear the front door opening and shutting.

Tealeaf Oooer! It's a ghost this time!

Caf It's probably the coppers seeing what all the noise is. Quick, hide!

Bazzer Where?

Caf The airing cupboard . . .

They hide in the airing cupboard. There is a pause. ***Mr Ali*** *comes in, switches the light on and looks around. He sees some gloves on the floor and picks them up. He goes to the bath and smiles. He pats the bath. He then goes to the door, switches the light off and goes. After a moment we hear the front door opening and shutting.* ***Bazzer, Tealeaf*** *and* ***Caf*** *reappear.*

Bazzer Phew, that was a close one.

Tealeaf My heart's still pounding. I reckon I'll have a heart attack at this rate!

Caf What was he doing nosin' around here?

Bazzer Well, it is his house!

Caf Oh, belt up!

Tealeaf It's dark, innit?

Caf Don't start that again! Tealeaf, take that end, I'll take this end. Right here we go. Up. Ooh. Right, now through the door. Bazzer, grab my end.

Pause.

Caf I meant my end of the *baf*!

Bazzer Oops, sorry, Caf.

They carry the bath away.

DIY Section

(See the explanation on page 4.)

Joe and Bazzer bring the pram. With Caf and Tealeaf, they load the bath on it.

Improvise the troubles and problems they have getting the bath through the night-time streets to Caf's house.

You may like to try some of these ideas:

1 A curious policeman stops them. They pretend they are training for a charity bath pushing race.

2 They pretend to be rag-and-bone men to avoid attention. People start coming out with all sorts of household junk and put it in the bath demanding money for it!

3 They try to get the bath on a bus. They are told that they can't. They have an argument with the driver or conductor.

4 While they are taking a rest, a policeman points out that they have stopped on a double yellow line and gives them a parking ticket.

5 They leave the bath for a moment. It begins to roll down a hill and into someone's garden, destroying flowers, etc. How do they get the bath back and deal with the irate person?

You will no doubt think of lots of ideas yourselves! Try out as many ideas as you can, and choose the best one.

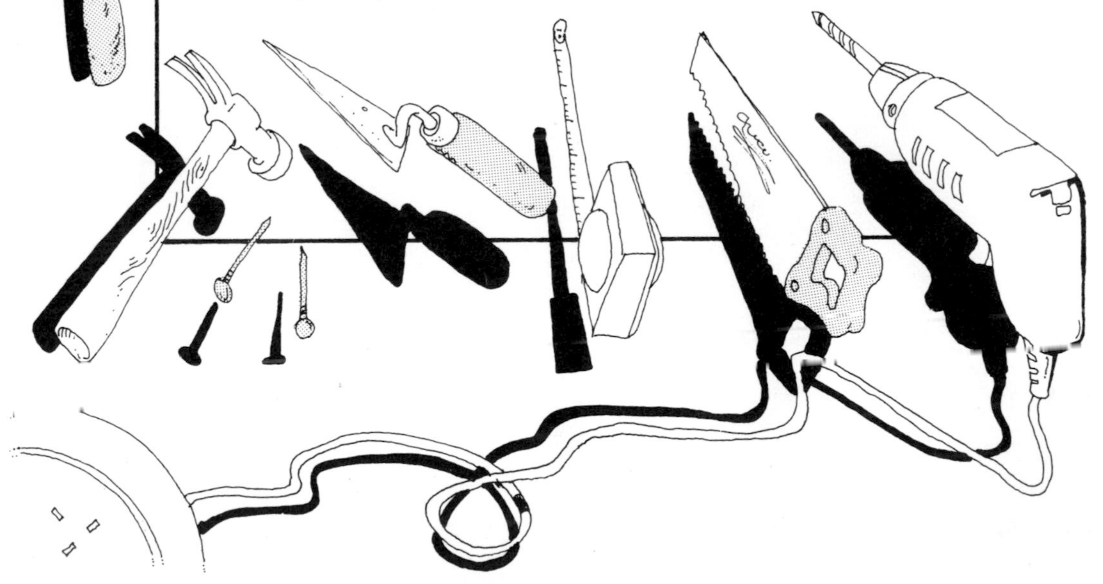

Scene 4

Next day. The back room of the paper shop. ***Caf, Bazzer, Tealeaf*** *and* ***Joe*** *are giggling.* ***Rodge-ah, Shammy, Yakki*** *and* ***Sharon*** *come in.*

Shammy What's funny?

Caf, Bazzer, Joe *and* ***Tealeaf*** *snigger.*

Yakki Come on, let us in on it.

Bazzer *tiptoes to the door to check Mr Ali is not around.*

Caf Is it all right?

Bazzer Yeah, he's serving Mrs Higgins, she'll keep him talking for ages.

Tealeaf Guess what we did last night. Me and Caf.

Bazzer And me!

Joe And me as well.

Tealeaf (*To* ***Joe*** *and* ***Bazzer***) You don't count.

Bazzer Thanks.

Joe Yeah, it *was* my pram, remember.

Shammy Well, what *did* you do?

Tealeaf *(Proudly)* We nicked a bath from Ali's new house.

Yakki You what?

Tealeaf Nicked a bath. For Caf's mum.

Shammy Off Mr Ali?

Tealeaf Yeah, good innit?

Sharon That's terrible!

Caf Shut it, Guts!

Tealeaf Yeah, you goody-goody.

Sharon Well, it is! How would you like it if someone pinched your bath?

Caf They can have it, it's got a hole in it!

***Tealeaf, Bazzer** and **Caf** all dissolve into laughter. **Joe** laughs too, although he doesn't really know why.*

Sharon That's not funny, Caf. It's not like you to steal.

Caf It isn't stealing, really . . .

Sharon What is it then? I bet you only did it to get at Mr Ali . . .

Caf Shut up.

Shammy Sharon's right. Nicking a bath isn't really nicking, when it belongs to a Pakistani. That's what you think, isn't it?

Caf No, not really . . . I mean, DG said.

Shammy DG? Huh!

Caf DG said Ali was buying the house to put homeless families in and make a load of money by being a slum landlord.

Shammy *(Sarcastically)* Oh, I see. After his career as a drugs dealer, Mr Ali's now a slum landlord, is he? I'm getting out of here, you make the air smell. And I don't mean 'cos you haven't had a bath.

***Shammy** storms out.*

Sharon That goes for me as well.

***Sharon** follows Shammy.*

Caf Oi! Come back here you two! *(To Tealeaf and Joe)* They can't talk to me like that! I'll do 'em! *(To Rodge-ah)* What do you reckon then, wimpo? Reckon we've been naughty, do you?

Rodge-ah My father says that hooligans and thieves are bringing the country to its knees and we need more police and stronger punishments.

Caf Shut your trap! Go on, get out!

***Caf** chases **Rodge-ah** out of the shop. He goes but comes back to shout through the door.*

Rodge-ah Bring back flogging!

Caf Get out!

***Caf** chases him out again.*

Caf It's all right for him. He can afford to be all high and mighty. Snobby little wimp. His mum and dad are rolling in it.

Yakki My mum and dad haven't got much. They wouldn't steal though.

Tealeaf All right, goody-goody. I'm going to buy a coke. Want one?

Yakki No, I don't. Not now.

Tealeaf *(Threateningly)* Why not?

Yakki Not thirsty. Besides, Shammy's right, isn't he?

***Yakki** goes.*

Caf Wimps!

Tealeaf Do you reckon DG was right about the homeless families?

Caf *(Not too sure)* 'Course he was.

Bazzer Hey, watch it, he's coming!

__Bazzer, Caf, Tealeaf__ and __Joe__ adopt positions of suspicious innocence. __Mr Ali__ walks in. He looks worried and unhappy.

Caf Good morning, Mr Ali.

Tealeaf Good morning, Mr Ali.

Mr Ali What? Oh yes, good morning. Have you got your papers yet?

Tealeaf Yeah, but you've given me Bakewell Close twice and nothing for Ross Street.

Mr Ali Oh, I'm sorry, Pauline, I'm afraid I'm making a lot of mistakes today. I'm a little upset.

Bazzer Why's that, Mr Ali? You lost something?

__Tealeaf__ and __Joe__ can hardly keep straight faces. __Caf__ kicks Bazzer.

Mr Ali As a matter of fact I have. How did you know?

Bazzer Er, just a lucky guess, I suppose.

The shop bell rings.

Bazzer Oh, there's the shop bell, Mr Ali. Shall I see who it is?

__Bazzer__ goes very quickly.

Mr Ali Now, Bakewell Close you said, Pauline?

__Bazzer__ comes back in. He is looking worried. He is accompanied by the same __two police officers__ who appeared in 'Paper Tigers'.

Police 1 Good morning, sir. Ah, it's Mr Ali, isn't it? Hope that you've got no hard feelings over that little misunderstanding we had a few weeks back.

Mr Ali Not at all, officer.

Police 1 Now, what's all this about? The duty officer said that you wanted to report a theft. Not custard powder, I hope?

*The **police officers** laugh.*

Mr Ali No, not custard powder. I wish to report the theft of a bath.

*The **police officers** exchange glances.*

Police 2 A bath, you say?

Mr Ali That's right, a bath.

*The **police officers** exchange a 'we've got a right one here' glance. **Police 2** takes out a notebook. **Caf, Bazzer, Tealeaf** and **Joe** look worried.*

Police 2 Rightio, then, sir, can you describe this bath?

Mr Ali *(At a slight loss)* Well . . . it was a bath. Large, white . . . a bath . . .

Police 2 Any distinguishing marks or features?

Mr Ali I don't know. Oh, it had a white plug . . .

Police 2 *(Closes his notebook)* I see. Where was it taken from?

Mr Ali From my house, 17 Lynham Gardens, last night. It was there when I called round to look for my gloves at about eight o'clock. When I went round this morning, it was gone.

Police 1 Ah, so you weren't actually in the house when the bath was stolen?

Mr Ali No, of course not. I would have heard something.

Police 1 Not necessarily. Some of the kids round here would nick your bath even if you were in it! Pinch the lead from your pencil, half of them.

***Police 1** looks hard at **Caf** and **Tealeaf**, who seem very worried and uncomfortable.*

Police 2 A bath? That's a new one. Was the house locked, sir?

Mr Ali No, I'd left it open for the builders.

Police 2 Very careless of you.

Mr Ali Well, I didn't think there was anything to steal. It never occurred to me that anyone would steal a bath.

Police 1 They'd steal the paper off the walls, given half a chance. So, it's not breaking and entering then. It's theft, not burglary. Pity, they'd get longer for burglary.

Mr Ali Do you think there's any chance of recovering the bath?

Police 1 Well, to be honest, not really. It's not as if it's an unusual bath. It could be connected to any one of a thousand wastepipes, by now. We'll keep our ears open but I'd say it was pretty hopeless. You are covered by insurance, aren't you?

Mr Ali Not yet. I haven't moved in yet, so I hadn't bothered to take any out.

Police 1 Oh dear. Well, we'll do our best, Mr Ali. Good day.

The ***kids*** *are looking happier now. The* ***police officers*** *go.* ***Mr Ali*** *fusses with the papers.*

Mr Ali Ah well, that's that I suppose. Here you are, Pauline, just take these. I'll deliver Ross Street myself later this morning. Come on, or you'll never get your rounds done before school.

Mrs Perkes *comes in.*

Mrs Perkes Oh, Mr Ali, there you are. There was no one in the shop, except two police officers, and so I wondered if you'd heard me, so I came in to see . . . ah, hello Caf. How are you?

Caf Okay, thanks.

Mrs Perkes Oh good. Did you get that bath home last night?

***Mr Ali** looks shocked. **Caf, Bazzer, Joe** and **Tealeaf** make for the door.*

Mrs Perkes I saw you from my bedroom window, I thought what a funny thing to be bringing home at that time of night. I suppose you got it from an ad in the paper . . .

Mr Ali *Catherine! Pauline! Barry! Joe!* Come back here. I want a word with you!

*But they have gone. **Mr Ali** chases after them. **Mrs Perkes** is left alone.*

. . . .

Scene 5

*A very run-down cafe, 'The Greasy Spoon'. **Caf, Tealeaf** and **Joe** are holding mugs. **Bazzer** is leaning back on a chair in an elaborate attitude of unconcern. He is throwing a tennis ball from one hand to the other and catching it in a glove.*

Joe What time is it?

Tealeaf Six o'clock.

Joe What time's this place close?

Caf We've been here five flamin' hours now.

Tealeaf That woman behind the counter keeps giving us funny looks.

Joe My mam'll kill me.

Caf Join the club.

Joe I reckon this was a daft idea of Bazzer's, going into hiding. We should've gone straight home.

Tealeaf Oh yeah, and find the police waiting for us? No thanks.

Joe It's not as if we've killed somebody.

Caf It's all right for you. You haven't got a record. I've been to court before. For fightin'. They told me that next time I got into trouble, I'd be taken into care. Then there was that stuff with Ali and the drugs. That was DG's bright idea as well. I'll kill him when I see him.

Tealeaf I've got a record too. The magistrate told me I wouldn't get any more fines. She reckoned that next time I nicked something it'd be probation at least. Or a hostel. I don't want to go to a hostel.

Caf *(To Bazzer)* Will you stop chuckin' that flamin' ball! What stupid game are you playin' now?

***Bazzer** continues to throw the ball.*

Tealeaf He thinks he's Steve McQueen.

Caf What?

Tealeaf That film, 'The Great Escape'. It was on telly last week. Steve McQueen was the Cooler King – every time the Nazis put him in jail, he threw a ball and caught it like that. Only it was a baseball in the film.

Caf Grow up, Bazzer.

Bazzer They won't get nothing out of me.

Caf You what?

Bazzer Name, rank and serial number, that's all.

Caf His brain's died.

Tealeaf What brain?

***Mrs Roberts,** the owner of 'The Greasy Spoon', comes over from the counter.*

Mrs Roberts Haven't you lot got homes to go to?

Caf Er, we're waiting for someone.

Mrs Roberts Well, they'd better get here soon, 'cos we shut at half past.

Caf Yeah, okay.

Mrs Roberts Look, I don't make any money just out of people having their bums parked on my chairs.

Tealeaf Oh, all right, four teas please.

Mrs Roberts *(Through gritted teeth)* Mugs or cups?

Tealeaf Cups, please.

***Mrs Roberts** clears away their mugs.*

Mrs Roberts Two teas each since dinner time. They say kids have got loads of money these days. Hummph!

***Mrs Roberts** bustles away. Silence. **Caf** puts her earphones in and listens to her walkman.*

Joe Tealeaf? We shouldn't have done it, should we?

Tealeaf Shut up, Joe.

Joe I'm scared.

Tealeaf Me too.

Joe Perhaps we could tell him it was a joke.

Tealeaf Don't be stupid!

Joe He might believe it. Do you reckon he'd believe it, Bazzer?

Bazzer Barry Hughes, Captain, 47733615/C.

Tealeaf Drop dead, Bazzer.

***Shammy** and **Sharon** come on.*

Shammy Thought we'd find you here.

Caf You seen Ali?

Shammy Of course.

Sharon What are you doing here? Your mum's frantic, Caf. So is yours, Tealeaf.

Joe What about mine?

Sharon We haven't been to yours, but I bet she is.

Shammy I bet even Bazzer's mum and dad are worried.

Bazzer Barry Hughes, Captain, 47733615/C.

Shammy What's he on about?

Tealeaf Ignore him. He's being stupid.

Sharon So what *are* you doing here?

Caf Hidin'. We daren't go home 'cos of the police.

Sharon What police?

Caf *The* police. They'll be waiting for us at home by now . . .

Sharon Mr Ali didn't call the police.

Caf You what?

Shammy She's right. No police.

Caf You mean we've been sittin' here for five hours drinking cold washin' up water and Ali never phoned the police?

Shammy That's right. Whose idea was it to go into hiding, anyway?

Caf*, *Tealeaf *and* ***Joe*** *look at Bazzer. He stops throwing his ball for the first time and looks nervously round at them.*

Bazzer Well, how was I supposed to know . . . ?

Caf *goes for him and tries to ram his tennis ball down his throat. The others pull her off.* ***Mrs Roberts*** *comes over with the tea.*

Mrs Roberts Oi! We'll have no rowdiness in here! Come on, let's have you out.

Shammy Sorry. We're just having a bit of fun. How much for the tea?

Mrs Roberts Eighty pence.

Shammy *gives her the money.*

Shammy Can we have two more, please?

Mrs Roberts Huh!

Shammy And a Mars Bar?

Mrs Roberts Last of the big spenders. Well, hurry up. We shut in five minutes!

Mrs Roberts *takes more money from Shammy and returns to the counter.*

Caf *(To Bazzer)* You stupid great . . .

Shammy Shut up, Caf, we don't want to get thrown out.

Caf *glares at Shammy.*

Shammy Mr Ali wants to see you.

Caf Well he can get knotted.

Shammy He didn't phone the police.

Caf So what?

Shammy Why won't you see him?

Caf 'Cos he'll want an apology, won't he? Well I'm not giving him his baf back and I ain't saying I'm sorry to a . . . *(She stops suddenly.)*

Shammy Go on, say it.

***Caf** says nothing. **Shammy** gets up. **Caf** goes to stop him by putting a hand on his sleeve.*

Caf Shammy!

Shammy Don't touch me! *(Jerks his arm away)*

Caf I didn't mean . . .

Shammy Well, what *do* you mean? There's a word for people like you.

Caf Shut up, Shammy, or I'll do you.

Shammy 'Course you will. People like you always do. My family knows all about your sort. We've had bricks through the window, fireworks through the letter box. Go on then, hit me.

***Caf** is almost in tears.*

Caf I'm not like that!

Shammy Prove it.

Caf All right, I'll see him . . .

Shammy And say you're sorry?

Caf Whatever he wants . . .

Shammy Good.

***Shammy** goes, followed by **Sharon. Tealeat, Joe** and **Bazzer** follow more slowly with lots of backward glances at Caf. She stands with her head hanging down. **Mrs Roberts** comes across and waits for her to leave.*

Caf *(Very, very quietly)* I'm sorry, Shammy. I just can't help it.

***Caf** leaves.*

. . . .

Scene 6

*The back room of the paper shop. **Mr Ali** is sorting papers. He looks up as **Caf** comes in, then goes back to sorting papers. **Caf** stands still, head down. The silence grows. **Caf** finally breaks it.*

Caf Shammy says you want to see me.

Mr Ali Yes, Catherine.

There is another silence.

Caf Sorry I nicked your baf.

Mr Ali *(Gently and quietly)* Oh, I don't think you are. Not yet. But perhaps you will be.

Caf Are you threatening me?

Mr Ali Oh no. Not at all. That's the last thing I would want to do.

There is another pause.

Mr Ali Shamir tells me you thought I was going to rent out my house to homeless families . . . become a slum landlord. I wonder who told you that.

Caf Nobody.

Mr Ali Derek, I suppose.

Caf Who?

Mr Ali DG.

Caf *(Startled)* Is that his name?

Mr Ali Yes.

Caf I didn't know.

Mr Ali I see. It's not true.

Caf That his name's Derek?

Mr Ali No, his name *is* Derek. It's not true what he said about me.

Caf Oh.

Mr Ali You've not said it *wasn't* him who told you about slum landlords.

Caf I never said it *was*, neither!

Mr Ali No.

Another pause.

Caf Can I go now?

Mr Ali Would you like to know why I bought the house?

***Caf** shrugs.*

Mr Ali For my mother.

Caf *(Startled)* Eh?!

Mr Ali Well, we should all look after our mothers, shouldn't we?

Caf Er, yeah.

Mr Ali My mother and father came to England because there was a lot of trouble in their area: riots, murders. They were refugees in a way. They came here and my father became a hospital porter. He worked very long hours. I hardly saw him when I was a child, he was always working. We lived in bedsits and lodging houses as it was all they could afford. Eventually they got a council flat. It was in one of the new high rise blocks. It was small . . .

Caf We lived in a high rise.

Mr Ali Then you'll know what it was like. Lifts not working, vandalism. What upset my mother most of all was this: the hot water didn't work and for years the council didn't repair it. She hated being dirty, you see. Then last year, my father died.

There is another pause.

Mr Ali Your father died too, didn't he, Catherine?

Caf *(Quietly)* Yes.

Mr Ali So that left my mother on her own. Frightened and alone. But then my father's insurance money came in, and my uncles and I were able to put some more to it and buy a house for my mother. She was so excited. She'd never lived in a house and she was looking forward to moving in. But most of all she was looking forward to having a bath. A bath with hot water that always worked. Funny isn't it, how important small things become when you have to do without them?

***Caf** says nothing.*

Mr Ali All right, Catherine. That's all.

Caf What? But . . .

Mr Ali I thought you ought to know about the house and the bath.

Caf I didn't know. I mean, you can stop it out of my wages till you've got enough for a new one . . .

Mr Ali Thank you, but my mother is over sixty. I'm afraid by the time your wages add up to the cost of a new bath, she won't be around to enjoy it.

Caf Will you tell the police then?

Mr Ali No. I didn't intend to tell the police, anyway.

Caf What about my job?

Mr Ali I don't know. I haven't decided.

Caf Do you want me in tomorrow?

Mr Ali Yes. Come in for the rest of the week. We'll decide on Friday.

Caf Do you . . . ?

Mr Ali I don't think you're happy working for me. Perhaps you'll be better off in another shop. We'll decide on Friday.

Caf I didn't know it was for your mum. I'd never have nicked it if I'd known. I never thought.

Mr Ali No.

***Caf** is silent for a minute.*

Caf *(In a rush)* I can't bring it back, Mr Ali. I want to, but I can't. I'd have to tell my mum I nicked it. She's not well and it would, well it would . . . I can't . . . *(She sniffles.)*

Mr Ali No, I understand. I wouldn't want to upset your mother.

Caf Is your mum moving in soon?

Mr Ali Tomorrow. I'd hoped that the house would be ready, but of course, when the plumber came this morning . . . well, she's had to wait a long time for a working bath. I dare say that another couple of weeks won't hurt.

The shop bell rings.

Mr Ali Would you finish these papers off? I won't be a moment.

***Mr Ali** exits. **Caf** sorts a few papers. She is very upset. **Mr Cross**, a plumber, comes in.*

Mr Cross Ah, found you, at last.

Caf Eh! Are you the police?

Mr Cross 'Strewth, no! You came to see me last week, in the shop.

Caf Oh yeah, Mr Cross, the plumber.

Mr Cross I knew you worked here, so I thought I'd drop in and ask your gaffer where I could find you. Working late aren't you?

Caf Sort of.

Mr Cross Well, thing is, you were asking me about baths last week. Are you still interested?

Caf Er, yeah.

Mr Cross I've got one. This snobby old beggar up Michelmore Drive, I only put it in for her last year, nice bath, ceramic, ivory finish, gold taps . . .

Caf Gold taps?

Mr Cross Not real gold, of course, but a lovely bath. Anyway, she wants it taking out 'cos her neighbour's just had a jacuzzi so, of course, she's got to have one as well. So, there it is . . . fifty pounds to you.

Caf *(Automatically)* Thirty!

Mr Cross Forty pounds then. I'm cutting my own throat at that, so that's my last offer. If you want it, come round to the shop in the morning. See you.

He goes. ***Mr Ali*** *returns.*

Mr Ali Is everything all right, Catherine?

Caf Oh yeah, Mr Ali. Just a bloke I know.

Mr Ali Right. I'll start locking up then.

*He goes. **Caf** stands for a moment in thought. She looks at her walkman and sighs.*

Mr Ali *(From the other room)* Ready, Catherine?

Caf Yes, Mr Ali. I'm ready.

***Caf** goes.*

. . . .

Scene 7

*Outside Mr Ali's house. **Mr Ali** appears with his **mother**. Though they do not realize it, they are being watched by **Sharon** and **Bazzer**.*

Mr Ali Here it is, Mother.

She says nothing.

Mr Ali *(Coughs nervously)* It is a bit small, I'm afraid, but . . .

Mother Ali, it is beautiful.

Mr Ali *(Relieved)* Ah well, yes, not a bad little place, and very sound.

Mother Of course.

Mr Ali It's only a terrace, I'm afraid.

Mother I like neighbours close by.

Mr Ali There's no garden.

Mother At my age, who wants a garden?

Mr Ali Some of the rooms are very small . . .

Mother Then it will be cheaper to heat.

Mr Ali . . . and some of the windows don't fit very well, and the doors have shrunk in their frames, and the floorboards have probably got woodworm . . .

Mother All right! I hate it!

Mr Ali Mother!

Mother Well, what do you want me to say then, you silly boy? It is a wonderful house and I bless you and my brothers and sisters for getting it for me. It's perfect.

***Mr Ali** has been grinning through his mother's speech. When she finishes, though, he looks embarrassed.*

Mr Ali Ah, well. Not quite perfect, I'm afraid. I mean, not quite complete. The builders haven't brought the bath yet.

Mother *(Trying to hide her disappointment)* Oh.

Mr Ali I'm sure that it'll be here in a few days . . .

Mother *(Still disappointed)* Oh, I'm sure that it will. I've waited so long for a bath of my own, a little longer won't matter.

***Bazzer** and **Sharon** have heard all of this. Exit **Bazzer**. **Sharon** steps forward.*

Mr Ali So, Mother. Shall I show you the inside?

Sharon Good morning, Mr Ali.

Mr Ali *(Surprised)* Good morning, Sharon. I'd like you to meet my mother. We were just about to . . .

Sharon Hello, Mrs Ali. Would you mind just waiting for a minute before you go in?

Mr Ali Er, why?

Sharon Caf and the others have got a little surprise for you . . .

Mother *(To Mr Ali)* What is happening?

Mr Ali Apparently the boys and girls who deliver papers from my shop have organised some kind of reception committee . . .

Mother *(A little nervously)* Oh? What will it be?

Mr Ali I hate to think. Sharon, what *is* this surprise?

Sharon If I told you that, Mr Ali, it wouldn't be a surprise any more, would it?

There is a sound of music and cheering. The rest of the ***Tigers*** *(except for DG) come on in a procession. They are wheeling a bath (with gold taps) on Joe's pram. One of the* ***Tigers*** *has a tape recorder playing an appropriate processional piece of music. The bath is gift wrapped with a large ribbon. All the* ***Tigers*** *are cheering and whistling and humming along with the music.*

Sharon Here they are!

Mr Ali's *jaw drops and he stands open-mouthed in amazement. The* ***Tigers*** *call out to him.*

Bazzer Where d'you wannit, mate?

Tealeaf Here you are, Mr Ali.

Yakki Sorry, we're late!

Joe I wanted to bring it on my Vespa, but they wouldn't let me.

Shammy Hello, Mrs Ali.

Rodge-ah Don't park it there, there's a yellow line!

Caf *comes in a little behind the others. She is not joining in with the celebration. She looks quite pleased with herself, but a little apprehensive.*

Mother What is it, Ali? What is going on?

Mr Ali It looks like the Paper Tigers have brought you a new bath, Mother.

Mother *(Delighted)* You mean, this is for me! This bath! And look! Gold taps! This is wonderful!

Bazzer It was Caf, Mr Ali.

Caf *kicks him.*

Ow!

The other ***Tigers*** *agree.*

Sharon Caf got the baf, I mean bath, Mr Ali.

Tealeaf And the rest of us came to help bring it here . . .

Yakki . . . And to welcome Mrs Ali and hope she's happy in her new house.

Tealeaf Hey! I was going to say that!

Mother Thank you, thank you very much. You are all so kind. *(To Mr Ali)* You never told me how wonderful your paper children are.

Mr Ali I didn't know, until now.

Shammy Shall we get the bath inside, Mr Ali?

Bazzer Joe's dad says he'll connect it for you . . .

Mr Ali That's very kind, Joe. Thank you for asking him.

Joe I didn't, Caf did. *(**Caf** kicks him.)* Ow!

*The **two police officers** appear. **DG** follows them. He doesn't join the Tigers but stands watching.*

Police 1 Morning, sir. Sorry to bother you but we've received some information from an anonymous caller . . .

Tealeaf That means a grass . . .

Police 1 Just you be careful, young lady. We have reason to believe that your bath was stolen by one of your employees.

*The **Tigers** look nervous.*

Police 1 Our information suggests that it was taken by Catherine Beasley . . .

***Caf** turns to run but finds that **Police 2** has moved behind her. She is grabbed by the shoulder.*

Police 2 Got her!

Police 1 Right, let's have you coming down the station with us.

Mr Ali Just a moment, officer, there must be a mistake!

Police 1 Oh, no mistake, sir. I might've guessed from the beginning. She's got form, fighting. Once they start going wrong . . . Come on then, you.

Mr Ali Just a moment, officer. I can't see that Catherine could possibly have been involved in this theft.

Police 2 Our informant was very positive, sir.

Mr Ali But, it doesn't make sense! You see this bath?

Police 2 Be a bit hard to miss it, sir.

Mr Ali Well, all these boys and girls brought it here to replace the one I lost. And it was all Catherine's idea. Wasn't it?

The ***Tigers*** *all agree, except for* ***DG*** *who just stands still.*

Mr Ali It doesn't make sense for Catherine to steal my bath, then replace it with this one, which is a lot better than my old one! That would be like a thief stealing a five pound note and leaving a tenner.

Police 1 I suppose if you put it like that . . .

Mr Ali I do, officer.

Police 1 Better let her go, for now. Insufficient evidence. *(To Caf)* I'll be watching you!

The ***police*** *go. The* ***Tigers*** *congratulate Caf on her escape.*

Tealeaf Hey, that was great, Mr Ali!

Bazzer Yeah, you really told them.

Mr Ali It was the least I could do. But I don't like deceiving people, especially the police, so I hope that you won't put me in that position again.

Tealeaf, Bazzer, Joe *and* ***Caf*** *look embarrassed.*

Mother *(Not understanding what this is all about)* It is getting on, shall we get the bath inside? And look over my new house?

The ***Tigers*** *agree and wheel the bath off.* ***Mr Ali*** *gives his* ***mother*** *the key and she follows the* ***Tigers****.* ***Caf*** *has not gone with the rest. She* *stands facing Mr Ali.* ***DG*** *is still in the background.*

Mr Ali You've made my mother very happy, Catherine.

Caf *(Awkwardly)* Well, I heard about this baf . . .

Mr Ali *(Shaking his head)* The bath was important, of course, but the welcome was more important. *(Realizing there is something missing)* By the way, what's happened to your walkman?

Caf Oh, er, I've lost it. I must've left it on the bus or something . . .

Mr Ali I understand. I shan't forget. Are you coming in? *(**Caf** shakes her head)* Then I'll see you on Monday.

Caf *looks up and smiles.* ***Mr Ali*** *returns the smile and goes.* ***Caf*** *looks up and sees* ***DG*** *lurking in the background.*

Caf Come here, you!

DG *comes over, reluctantly.*

Caf Where've you been?

DG I've not been well.

Caf You never turned up!

DG I sent Bazzer!

Caf Big deal! And where were you when we were getting the baf?

DG I had a headache.

Caf You'll have more than that if you let the rest of us down. So, when did you get here?

DG Dunno.

Caf I do. You came in with those two coppers. I wonder why?

DG Sheer coincidence.

Caf *(Looks at him suspiciously)* I wonder who told them about me and the baf?

DG Don't look at *me*!

Caf If I thought for a minute that you'd grassed on me . . .

***Yakki** comes out of the house.*

Yakki Hey, Caf, Mr Ali's mum's all right! She's sent me out to get a bottle of coke and some crisps. Are you comin' with me?

DG *(To Caf)* Come off it, Caf, you know I wouldn't grass you up. Why don't you and me go down to the arcade while the little kids have their party with Curry Face . . . ?

***Caf** grabs the lapels of **DG**'s coat.*

Caf *(Very threateningly)* You will *never* call Mr Ali that again.

***Caf** lets him go and starts to walk off.*

Caf Come on, Yakki, let's get the crisps.

DG *(Very shaken)* What did I say?

Yakki Too much, pal.

***Yakki** pats DG on the cheek and follows Caf.*
***DG** is left standing alone.*

a Burn *Round* *the* Crem

The Characters

Caf		
DG		
Shammy		
Sharon		*the 'Paper Tigers'*
Kawasaki Joe		
Rodge-ah		
Bazzer		
Tealeaf		
Yakki-da		
Mr Ali	*	
Woman		*a potential customer*
Big Mal		
Meltin' Ice Cream		*Eggie Harris' gang*
Spanner		
Psycho		
Police 1	*	
Police 2	*	
Mrs Roberts		*owner of the 'Greasy Spoon' café*
Kawasaki Joe's brother		

* see **Paper Tigers**

Scene 1

The back room of Mr Ali's shop. ***Caf, Yakki, DG, Kawasaki Joe, Tealeaf, Rodge-ah, Shammy*** *and* ***Sharon*** *are collecting their papers.*

Joe *(To Yakki)* Did you see the racing on the telly on Saturday?

Yakki No. What was that?

Joe The motorbike Grand Prix. From Silverstone. It was brilliant!

Yakki No, I didn't see it. I was doing my homework.

Caf Homework? On Saturday! You shouldn't do your homework on Saturday.

Yakki Why not?

Caf 'Cos it don't have to be in the next day. You can't hand homework in on Sunday, 'cos we're not at school. Right?

The ***Tigers*** *are confused.*

Shammy All right, Caf. But, so what?

Caf 'But, so what?' You lot are really thick! No one does homework until the day before it's got to be handed in, of course.

The ***Tigers*** *are still not sure what Caf is on about.*

Caf *(Exasperated)* So, if it's due in on Thursday, you do it on Wednesday. If it's due in on Monday, you do it on Sunday, *not* Saturday!

Rodge-ah Actually, Caf, I do my homework on the day it's given me.

Caf *(Snapping)* Well, you would, you're not normal.

Tealeaf I don't do my homework the day before, either.

Caf Why not?

Tealeaf I never do my homework!

*The **Tigers** all burst out laughing except for **Caf**, who is struggling to keep her temper.*

Caf Yeah, okay, Tealeaf. But if you did, you wouldn't do it till the day before it had to be handed in, *would you*?

***Tealeaf** sees **Caf's** fist closing in on her nose.*

Tealeaf Er . . . No.

***Bazzer** walks in.*

Bazzer Hiya.

Joe Hi. Hey, Bazzer, did you see the motorcycling on the telly on Saturday?

Bazzer No. I was doing my homework.

***Caf** swings for him.*

Caf I'm gonna kill you!

***Bazzer** tries to avoid her.*

Bazzer What have I done? What's the matter?

***Caf** is stopped in her attempt to separate Bazzer's head from his body by the appearance of **Mr Ali**.*

Mr Ali What's all the noise? Catherine, leave him alone. Why are you all standing about? I want the papers delivering. So, get a move on everybody!

***Mr Ali** walks out. The **Tigers** finish collecting their papers.*

Caf He's in a right mood.

DG So, what's new?

Caf Shut it, DG.

Rodge-ah I wonder what's bothering him.

Sharon He's not been in a good mood for ages.

Yakki Hey, I'm three papers short. Who's nicked them?

Shammy I'm short as well.

Bazzer No you're not. You're taller than me!

Caf Shut up, Bazzer, your jokes are pathetic.

Yakki I'll go and see what's happened to them.

***Yakki** goes to fetch Mr Ali.*

Shammy I've been delivering less papers recently. 25 Wogan Way cancelled theirs last week. Too expensive they reckoned.

Sharon The bloke at 14 Rippon Rise told me that he wasn't having them any more. He said that there wasn't enough news in them. More like comics he said.

Rodge-ah My father believes that the only papers worth reading are the *Times* and the *Financial Times*.

Caf Oh ladi da! Shut up, Rodge-ah, you wimp!

***Mr Ali** and **Yakki** enter.*

Yakki I'm three missing, Mr Ali.

Mr Ali They're not missing, Gareth, they're cancelled. People don't want the papers.

Caf Why not?

Mr Ali Lots of reasons, I suppose. We lost a lot of customers when they knocked down the Valley Estate flats and built the shopping centre. If we continue to lose customers then you'll be delivering fewer papers.

DG That's good.

Caf Yeah, makes it easier.

Mr Ali It isn't good. Less papers means less money. That means that I can't afford to keep you all on.

There is a silence.

Caf What do you mean?

Mr Ali I won't be able to afford to pay you all. I'll have to ask some of you to leave.

The ***Tigers*** *react.*

Caf What! You mean we'll get the sack?

Mr Ali I'm afraid so.

Tealeaf But how will I pay my fines if I'm not working?

Mr Ali You won't all go. Just some of you.

The ***Tigers*** *look at each other.*

Shammy Who?

Sharon Yes, how will you decide?

Mr Ali I don't know. It's been worrying me for days. I don't know how I can make it fair.

There is a pause.

Shammy Do you *have* to sack some of us?

Mr Ali I can't afford to keep you all on. I don't want to lose any of you, but

I don't see what else I can do.

Rodge-ah Couldn't you pay us less?

Caf What!

Tealeaf Get lost!

DG No way!

Mr Ali You see the reaction that that idea gets! Anyway, I wouldn't consider it. You work hard and deserve decent pay.

DG Yeah, we do. Besides, we don't get paid as much as Eggie Harris's lot.

Tealeaf Old baldy Harris? You mean Harris's Newsagents on the Hill Estate?

DG Yeah.

Tealeaf Who'd want to work for him? He's a nutter!

DG He pays more, though.

Shammy But you have to deliver loads more papers and cover for anyone if they get ill.

DG He still pays more . . .

There is a silence.

Sharon I've got an idea! Why don't we get some more customers!

Mr Ali It's a good idea, Sharon, but where from?

Caf I know, what about the Hill Estate?

Tealeaf Yeah, it's massive. I bet we can get loads up there.

Mr Ali We can't. That's Mr Harris's area. We have an agreement about areas. He doesn't come into my area and I don't go into his. It's been agreed.

Bazzer That's like a film I saw the other night. It was all about the Mafia and their rackets.

Joe What sort of racquets? Tennis?

Bazzer No, dopehead. Protection rackets. One gang started a racket in their area, then another gang tried to take it over. That's when the fighting started. Machine guns, blood and guts! It was brilliant!

Caf Shut up, Bazzer.

Mr Ali Well, we certainly don't want blood and guts round here, thank you.

Shammy Hey, I've just thought. What about that new road they've just built? Coleman Crescent.

Mr Ali Where's that?

Shammy Next to the Hill Estate, but it's new and it's massive . . .

Mr Ali Show me where it is.

They go to a map on the wall.

Shammy Look, there it is . . .

Mr Ali You're right, it isn't part of the Hill Estate.

Sharon So we could deliver papers there, couldn't we?

Caf We'll go round advertising them. Knock on the doors and ask people if they want a paper. Now who's going to go?

The ***Tigers*** *look at each other.*

Yakki I'll go. I'm the newest.

Mr Ali Thank you.

Caf Well done, Yakki.

Bazzer He can't go on his own.

Tealeaf Why not?

Bazzer 'Cos in the film when a gang member went to explore a new area, he got ambushed. He was beaten up by the other gang. Blood and guts everywhere!

Caf Bazzer, don't be stupid!

Tealeaf He's right, Caf, it could be dangerous.

Yakki What's dangerous about knocking on doors?

Bazzer You never know.

Tealeaf Yeah. Eggie Harris's lot hang around that area. Some of them are bigger nutters than Eggie!

Rodge-ah Especially Big Mal.

Yakki Who's he?

Rodge-ah The gang leader. And there's Psycho.

Yakki *Who*?

Caf Psycho. Huh, she's no trouble. She's all talk.

Rodge-ah I'd be scared to meet her on a dark night.

Caf You'd be scared to meet a poodle on a clear day, you wimp.

Bazzer Well, I still think he needs protection. You need a minder. Like on the telly. Arthur Daley's got a minder who looks after him.

Mr Ali Do you really think it's necessary?

Bazzer You never know. Better safe than sorry.

Caf All right, Bazzer, you go with him. You know all about it.

Bazzer What! You're joking! I can't. I mean, er . . .

Caf You're not scared, are you?

Bazzer Yes! I mean no! It's just that . . . er . . . er . . . Oh yeah, I've got to do some homework.

Caf When's it got to be in?

Bazzer Friday.

Caf Well you can do it on Thursday! It's settled. Yakki, you're going up Coleman Crescent to get some customers. Our jobs depend on it!

*The **Tigers** take their bags and all leave. **Mr Ali** watches them go.*

. . . .

Scene 2

*Coleman Crescent. **Yakki** is at the door of a **woman** who is a potential customer. **Bazzer** is at the gate looking up and down the street. He is wearing a long coat and sunglasses, and carrying a violin case.*

Woman Well, I'm not sure.

Yakki We'll deliver a paper every day. It doesn't cost much and it saves you the bother of collecting one from a shop.

Woman Go on then, you've persuaded me.

Yakki Great! Here's a form to fill in. Just put your name on it and the paper you want. I'll pick it up tomorrow and start delivering the paper next week.

Woman Thank you. Er, excuse me, but is your friend all right?

Yakki Oh, you mean Bazzer. It's hard to say really.

Woman Why is he hiding behind my bush wearing sunglasses when it's nearly dark? And why has he got a violin case?

Yakki He wants people to think he's got a machine gun in it.

Woman Has he?

Yakki No, he's got a violin in it.

Woman Seems daft to me.

Yakki *(Changing the subject)* So, I'll pick up the form tomorrow. Cheerio.

***Yakki** runs down the path. The **woman** goes back into the house. **Bazzer** grabs hold of Yakki.*

Yakki What are you doing?

Bazzer Checking that the coast is clear.

Yakki You're cracked!

Bazzer Listen, did you persuade her?

Yakki Yes.

Bazzer Great! That's ten so far. At this rate, Mr Ali won't have to sack any of us.

Yakki Come on, we've still got loads more houses to do.

Bazzer Oh no!!

Yakki What's the matter?

Bazzer Let's get out of here, quick!

Yakki Why?

Bazzer *(Pointing)* It's them. Eggie Harris's lot. Oh no, Big Mal's there. And Psycho! She's worse than Rambo and Godzilla together! I'm off!

__Bazzer__ starts to run off.

Yakki Oi! I thought you were supposed to be my minder.

Bazzer *(Shouting back)* Yeah. I'm minding my own business!

__Yakki__ starts to follow him but he's too late. Eggie Harris's gang have entered and surrounded him. There are four of them: two boys, __Big Mal__ and __Meltin' Ice Cream__, and two girls, __Spanner__ and __Psycho.__ __Big Mal__ acts and talks like an imitation gangster.

Big Mal Is that your companion who is leaving this vicinity at a rapid rate of knots?

Yakki Hey?

Meltin' He said, is that your mate runnin' away?

Yakki Why didn't he say so, then?

Big Mal Who might you be?

Yakki Gareth.

Meltin' I've heard of you. You're one of them lot from Ali's paper shop, aren't you?

Yakki Might be.

Psycho Don't get smart or else Mal will rip your head off, won't you, Mal?

__Big Mal__ stares at __Psycho__. She becomes apologetic.

Psycho Sorry, Mal.

Big Mal *(To Psycho)* Thank you. *(To Yakki)* Now then, I believe that you are called Yakki.

Psycho Yakki! What a stupid name! Ain't that a stupid name, Mal? Go on, let me hit him for havin' such a stupid name!

__Big Mal__ stares at her again.

Psycho Sorry, Mal.

Big Mal What are you doing here, anyway?

Yakki Nothing.

Psycho He's lying, Mal! Let's get the truth from him. Let me rip his tongue out, then he'll tell us!

Big Mal Psycho! Be quiet will you! If we rip his tongue out, how will he be able to tell us anything? He won't be able to speak!

Psycho Oh yeah. Sorry, Mal.

Big Mal I don't know why I bother with you, I really don't. You're absolutely stark raving mad.

Psycho Thanks, Mal, that's the nicest thing you've said to me.

__Big Mal__ shakes his head in disbelief. He turns back to Yakki.

Big Mal Now then, what are you doing trespassing on our patch?

Yakki *(Making it up as he goes along)* Er, oh yeah . . . I was just visiting my auntie who lives up here and I didn't know the way so Bazzer showed me but then he had to rush off for his violin lesson.

Mal's gang *look unsure about this.*

Big Mal Are you sure?

Yakki *(Nodding furiously)* Oh yeah, dead sure. So I'll get off then and see my auntie.

Yakki *starts to back away.*

Big Mal All right, but if I catch you here again . . .

Yakki You won't. Promise.

Yakki *gets further away. Just then the* ***woman*** *comes in holding the form Yakki had given her.*

Woman Oh, there you are! Glad I caught you.

Mal's gang *look at each other.* ***Yakki*** *realizes that he is in big trouble.*

Woman We'll have a morning and an evening paper. I've filled the form in, like you said.

Big Mal *begins to move in.*

Yakki Oh hello, auntie. How are you?

Woman Auntie? What are you on about? You're as daft as your friend! Do you want this or not?

Big Mal *takes the form. He looks at it.*

Big Mal Of course he does, madam. Thank you very much.

*The **woman** goes off. **Mal's gang** surround Yakki.*

Big Mal Just visiting your auntie, hey? Do you like hospital food?

Yakki Dunno. Why?

Big Mal Because you are going to be eating a lot of it. Psycho! Kill!

***Psycho** goes for Yakki but is stopped by a shout.*

Caf Touch him and you're dead!

***Caf, Shammy, Sharon, Tealeaf, Rodge-ah, Joe, DG** and **Bazzer** rush in.*

Caf I said leave him.

Bazzer *(To Yakki)* I told you I was your minder.

Big Mal What are you doing on our territory?

Tealeaf Look, Coleman Crescent is just as near to our area as it is to yours. And it's new, so it isn't anybody's.

Big Mal I don't care. We are claiming this area for our shop.

Caf Says who?

Psycho Rip 'er to bits, Mal!

***Mal** begins to move towards Caf. The two gangs prepare themselves for a fight. Just then the two **police officers** we have met before in* Paper Tigers *and* Caf's Baf *appear.*

Tealeaf Watch out, it's the law!

The two groups quickly break apart. They all look suspicious.

Police 1 All right! What's going on here?

Big Mal Nothing at all, officer.

Police 2 Looked to me as though they were about to have a fight.

Police 1 I couldn't agree more. *(He recognizes **Caf**)* You! Catherine Beasley! I might have guessed. Up to no good again, I bet!

Caf No. I was just havin' a chat with my mate, wasn't I?

__Caf__ digs Big Mal in the ribs.

Big Mal Watch it! I mean . . . oh yes, that is correct, officer, a little chat.

Police 1 Do you usually chat with your fists?

Psycho *(Quietly)* I do.

Police 1 I beg your pardon?

Psycho Achoo! I sneezed.

Police 1 Be careful, young lady. Right, clear off the lot of you or you'll be coming down the station with us.

Caf Can I just finish my chat with my friend?

Police 1 I suppose so. Hurry up though.

__Caf__ and __Big Mal__ go to the side and begin to talk. The others look on.

Yakki *(To Bazzer)* I thought I was in big trouble there.

Bazzer No sweat. I had it all under control.

Shammy You lying hound! You bumped into us by accident, outside the shop.

Yakki Is that right?

Bazzer Not quite . . .

Yakki Well thanks, Bazzer. You're gonna need a minder, to stop me from getting you. Some mate you are!

__Caf__ and __Mal__ finish their talk.

Police 1 Right, let's have you off.

__Mal's gang__ leave. The __police__ go as well.

Caf I've arranged a meeting with Big Mal to sort this out.

Yakki When?

Caf Tomorrow at six at the Greasy Spoon Caff. Big Mal and Spanner and me and DG.

The __Tigers__ begin to leave.

Bazzer This is brilliant! It's just like that film. Gang warfare! Meetings, deals, taking over! Blood and guts! It's great!

Caf Bazzer, shut up will you or else it'll be your blood and guts!

The __Tigers__ leave.

. . . .

Scene 3

The Greasy Spoon Café. __Caf__ and __DG__ are sitting at a table.

DG I don't see why we have to do this.

Caf 'Cos we've got to save our jobs.

DG We can always get jobs somewhere else. Eggie Harris would have us, straight away.

Caf I'm not working for him. Anyway, I want to get more customers for Mr Ali, so he doesn't lose money and have to sell up like Mrs Green.

DG So what? I don't care if he does . . .

Caf *is about to reply when* ***Big Mal*** *and* ***Spanner*** *walk in.*

Caf Here they are. Stay cool.

Mal *and* ***Spanner*** *arrive at the table.*

Big Mal Here we are then, Caferine. Let's talk, shall we?

Caf Yeah. Sit down.

Mal *and* ***Spanner*** *sit down.*

Big Mal There was a problem yesterday, Caferine; you were trespassing on our area.

Caf No, we weren't. Coleman Crescent isn't part of the Hill Estate, it's next to it, so it ain't your patch.

Spanner And it ain't yours either.

Caf *(Angrily)* Oh yeah, and what are you gonna do about it?

Mrs Roberts, *owner of the Greasy Spoon, comes over.*

Mrs Roberts Oi you lot! Keep the noise down or I'll chuck you out. *(She sees Caf)* Oh, it's you, is it? I hope you're going to buy something this time. Last time you were in here you didn't have a thing.

Caf Sorry. We'll have four teas please.

Mrs Roberts *goes back to her counter.*

Caf Look, we need those customers from Coleman Crescent, otherwise we'll lose our jobs.

Spanner Aah, didums!

Caf But if we lose our jobs at Mr Ali's, then we'll come over to your shop and take *your* jobs!

Big Mal I don't think so. Eggie wouldn't have you lot working for him. Besides, we want those customers for ourselves.

Caf Why?

Spanner 'Cos Eggie's promised us a quid for every new customer we get.

Big Mal And there's a lot of houses on Coleman Crescent, which means a sizable amount of spondooleys!

Spanner So you ain't having it!

Caf But we ain't gonna let you have it either!

***Big Mal** looks at DG.*

Big Mal What's your opinion, DG?

DG I think we ought to fight for it.

Caf Are you bananas? We can't fight. You heard what the law said. They're watching out for us.

DG I don't mean that sort of fighting.

Caf What do you mean then?

DG In the olden days when two armies met, instead of the armies fighting, they'd both choose a champion. The champions would fight each other and the winner won the battle and the losers had to surrender. Like David and Goliath. We could have a sort of competition.

Caf Well, fighting's out.

Spanner That's a pity. Psycho would smash you any day.

Caf Yeah?

Spanner Yeah.

***Mrs Roberts** comes over with the teas.*

Mrs Roberts I've told you lot, keep it down. That'll be ninety-six pence.

They sort out the money and give it to her. She goes back to the counter.

Caf Let's decide what kind of competition we're going to have. *(To Mal)* You go over there with Spanner and sort out what you lot are good at, and we'll sort out what we're good at.

Big Mal That seems satisfactory.

***Big Mal** and **Spanner** go to another table.*

Caf Well, what are we good at?

DG Dunno. Bazzer's good at watching telly.

Caf *(Shouts)* How about a telly quiz?

Big Mal You must be joking!

Mrs Roberts Keep the noise down!

Caf Sorry. Well, what about Tealeaf? She must be good at something.

DG Nicking, that's about all.

Big Mal *(Shouts)* How about swimming?

Caf *(To DG)* Any good?

DG Don't think so.

Caf *(Shouts)* No!

Mrs Roberts I won't tell you again!

Caf Sorry! Hey what about Rodge-ah? He's good at dancing. We could have a dancing competition.

DG We'd get laughed at. Hang on, what about Joe? His bike! We could challenge them to a motorbike race.

Caf Yeah! Brilliant idea! Joe's great on bikes, he's bound to win.

DG Let's try it.

Caf Oi, Mal, come here.

***Big Mal** and **Spanner** return.*

Caf How about a motorbike race?

***Big Mal** and **Spanner** smile. So does **DG**.*

Big Mal Sounds interesting, go on.

Caf Joe does a bit of riding and he's got his own Vespa. If you've got anyone with a bike, they could race against Joe.

Big Mal Hmm, an interesting proposition. *(Deliberately to Spanner)* I wonder if we have got any particular person who may be able to take up this challenge?

Spanner *(Deliberately)* Um, oh yes. Hasn't Dave got a bike?

Big Mal Oh good heavens, so he has. I think, Caferine, you have yourself a deal.

Caf Right then, a race. Where?

DG How about two laps round the crematorium? It's quiet there.

Big Mal It would be, it's a crematorium!

DG We'll have to race on Sunday as there's no funerals then.

Big Mal That sounds satisfactory.

Caf All right, a burn round the crem. Joe versus your rider. First past the post takes the customers for their shop.

Big Mal That sounds fair, doesn't it, Spanner?

Spanner *(Laughing)* Oh yeah, dead fair.

Big Mal Good. Cheerio. Be seeing you, DG.

Big Mal *and* ***Spanner*** *go.*

Caf What's he mean by that?

DG Dunno.

Joe, Bazzer *and* ***Tealeaf*** *come rushing in.*

Tealeaf What's the crack?

Caf We've got a challenge. A bike race. Joe, you're gonna race against their champion. Two laps round the crem on Sunday. The first past the post wins the customers on Coleman Crescent.

Joe Brill! So who's their challenger?

Caf Dunno. They said his name was Dave.

Joe Dave? Dave Dunn?

Caf They didn't say.

Joe I bet it is. Only, he ain't known as Dave, he's known as Meltin' Ice Cream.

Caf Meltin' Ice Cream? Why's he called that?

Joe Nothin' moves faster than meltin' ice cream.

Caf You mean he's good at racin'?

Joe You bet he is! He's in a bike club. He's got a mega bike and he does displays and formation riding and that. And there's Spanner . . .

Caf What about 'er?

Joe She's the best mechanic I've ever seen. She could get fifty miles an hour out of a shopping trolley!

Caf *(To DG)* You wally! Why didn't you say?

DG You didn't ask.

Caf Didn't ask! Did you know?

DG Of course not. I'd have said if I knew, wouldn't I?

Caf What are we gonna do? We can't back out now.

Bazzer We'll just have to get Joe fighting fit. A human machine. I saw a film on it. The riders have got to have muscles like iron. They had to do loads of exercises and run and all that sort of thing.

Joe What!

Caf That's settled then. Tealeaf, you've got to make sure that Joe's fit for Sunday. He's got to win this race or else we'll lose our jobs. Come on, we'll start the training *now*!

***Caf** and **Tealeaf** go out with **Joe** who is moaning away.*

DIY Section

(See the explanation on page 4.)

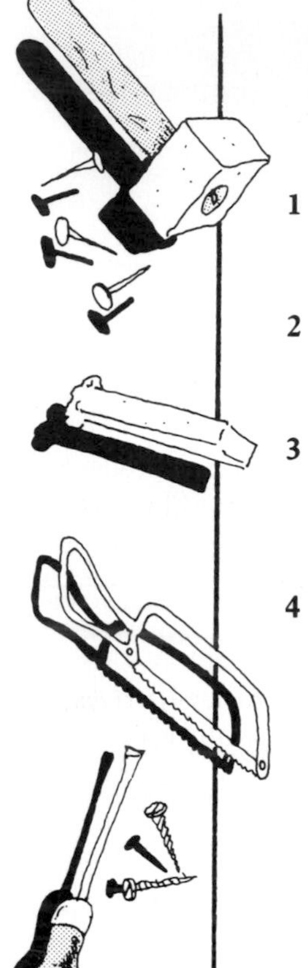

Joe has to get fit! Tealeaf is given the task of doing this. Improvise some scenes in which Joe tries to get out of the training.

Here are some ideas that you might like to explore:

1. Joe has to go on a crash diet. His favourite food is beefburgers. He is dying for a beefburger. Tealeaf orders a guard on the local café so Joe can't sneak in. How does Joe get past this? Is he discovered?
2. Joe is ordered on early morning training runs. He would prefer to stay in bed! How does Tealeaf make sure that he gets up and goes running? What excuses do the Tigers give to Joe's parents when they go round in the morning?
3. Joe is put onto a strict fitness course. This involves training like a boxer, because Tealeaf has seen boxers train on TV. She forces Joe to do circuit training in the school gym. The P.E. teacher is astonished: Joe never usually does P.E.
4. Tealeaf thinks that Joe ought to join the Army Cadets in order to get on their assault course training and so get fit. How does she persuade Joe to go for an interview? Does he pass this? How does he cope with the assault course?

You can try some or all of these ideas. We'd prefer you to think of your own and use them.

Scene 4

The Crematorium. The **Tigers** *enter carrying various items: flags, oil cans, cones, ear protectors, spare parts etc.* **Joe** *is not with them.*

Bazzer We're gonna do this properly.

Caf I thought you said you were going to organize it.

Bazzer Yeah.

Caf Then how are we gonna do it properly?

Bazzer I've seen it all on telly. I watch all of 'em. Alain Prost, Nigel Mansell, Ayrton Senna . . .

DG That's motor racing, banana head!

Bazzer Cars, bikes, it's all the same innit? Look, stop arguing. Caf, Shammy and Yakki, you're marshals, right?

Shammy Okay. Come on, pardner, guess we'd better mosey on over to the old corral – yep! *(Does a John Wayne walk.)*

Caf What're all these flags for?

Bazzer You start the race with the Union Jack and finish it with the chequered one.

Shammy We know that, what about the blue one and the yellow one?

Bazzer The blue one means there's a bike trying to get past . . .

Caf What about the yellow one?

Bazzer That's for danger.

Caf Joe won't be in any danger unless he loses. Then I'll belt him!

Shammy What about the red one?

Bazzer *(Enthusiastically)* That's for stopping the race if anyone gets killed.

Shammy *drops the flag in disgust and wipes his hand on his jumper.*

Caf You berk! You don't need that. They're only going round the crem.

Bazzer Gotta be prepared for anything! Right, now we've got to organize a pit stop.

Tealeaf A pit stop! Flippin' 'eck, they're only doing two laps!

Bazzer But they always have a pit stop . . . What if he gets a puncture, eh? What if he needs a wheel changing?

Tealeaf We haven't got a spare wheel, anyway!

Bazzer Yeah, well, you never know. DG, Tealeaf, you're in the pits. *(Gives Tealeaf a blackboard and chalk)* That's the race position board, you write down the numbers of the riders in race order so they can see who's leading.

Tealeaf But there's only two of them! They're gonna know who's in front, aren't they? 'Cos if they're not in front, they're behind, and if they're not behind, they're in front.

Bazzer Eh?

Tealeaf What I mean is, if they're in front, there's nobody in front of them, but if there's somebody in front of them, they're not in front, they're behind.

Shammy Er . . . Could you explain that again?

Tealeaf I've forgotten what we were talking about!

Bazzer Just write the race order and the lap times. Rodge-ah gets the stop watch, he times the laps an' you show it on the board to Joe the next time he comes through the pits . . .

Rodge-ah But the next time he comes through the pits, the race will be over.

Bazzer Do you want to do this properly or not?

The others shrug.

Bazzer Right, then.

Sharon What do I do?

Bazzer You present the winner with a sash.

Sharon A what?

Bazzer One of those big ribbons, and a wreath and a bottle of champagne.

Sharon Bottle of champagne?

Bazzer Well, a can of coke.

Sharon And where am I supposed to get a wreath from?

Bazzer Gimme strength! We're in the *crem*, Guts, there's wreaths everywhere!

Sharon I'm not taking one of them! That's robbing the dead. I'll make a daisy chain or something.

Bazzer I don't believe this.

Caf (*To Bazzer*) What are you doin'?

Bazzer I'm doing the commentary. *(Does a Murray Walker impersonation.)* Hello from the crematorium, and Barry is here with me . . .

The others groan and cover their ears.

Caf Leave it out, Bazzer.

A motorcycle is heard off.

Caf Look, here comes Joe.

Bazzer Get him to park his bike down there and bring him up here.

***Caf** exits.*

Bazzer Shammy, get on the hill. Yakki, you go to the start of the straight.

The motorcycle approaches, then stops. ***Caf*** *brings* ***Joe*** *in.*

Bazzer Come on, Joe, we're doing a sprint start. You run to your bike . . .

Joe Sprint? In my condition? I'm shattered!

Bazzer All right, stagger . . . anyway, get to your bike, start it up, down the straight, hang a left at Doris-Evans-Sadly-Missed, up the hill, left at the Chapel of Rest, right at Fred-Henshaw-With-The-Angels, down the hill, through the coke pile chicane, left at the big marble job with the cherubs on top, right at Mary-Birtles-RIP, down the finishing straight and start again. Got it?

Joe Er . . .

Bazzer Good. Union Jack, Caf.

Caf *gets it.*

Ready, steady, *go*!

Caf *waves the flag.* ***Joe*** *totters off.* ***DG, Sharon, Tealeaf*** *and* ***Rodge-ah*** *cheer Joe on and groan etc throughout* ***Bazzer's*** *commentary.*

Bazzer *(Being Murray Walker)* And there goes Kawasaki Joe, down the hill, he leaps onto his machine . . . Ooh that brought tears to his eyes . . . he pumps the kick start *(Motorcycle engine sound effects)* and he's off, tyres squealing, up the straight, left up the hill . . . I thought he took that turn rather wide, Barry . . . *(As himself)* Yes, not at all the line I would have taken . . . *(As Murray Walker)* I'll have to cut in, Barry, because Joe has reached the last resting place of Stanley Gutteridge, and he flicks the mighty Vespa smoothly round . . . What's he doing now, Barry? *(As himself)* Picking his nose, I think, no, no, he's wiping his visor. *(As Murray Walker)* Fantastic! He's past the Chapel of Rest, smoke pouring out of where his turbo would be if he had one . . . *(As himself)* I think he may regret the decision to fit smooth tyres in these conditions, Murray . . . *(As*

Murray Walker) ... and now he's into the chicane, sliding a bit on the coke dust ... Ooh that was a *nasty* skid, but he's clear now ... just a minute! There's something leaking from the bike ... would you say that was brake fluid, Barry? *(As himself)* No, I think he's wet himself! *(As Murray Walker)* Astonishing! And now he's coming into the finishing straight, one more lap to go, here he comes ... And there he goes! *(As himself)* Got the time, Rodge-ah? Write it down, Tealeaf. *(As Murray Walker)* He's really motoring now and he ... *(The sound of a horrendous crash)* Oh, now, what? I think ... yes, his engine's blown up! Well, isn't that amazing ... what do you think, Barry? *(As himself)* Well, I did detect a rather dodgy note in his engine as he went past ...

***Joe** enters, staggering, shocked, holding the handlebars.*

Bazzer *(As Murray Walker)* Well, I'll try and see if I can get through the pit crew and have a word. What happened, Joe?

Joe Urrrrrrrrrr!

Bazzer Terrific! Well, I have with me the leader of Joe's team. Caf, what do you think this will do to Joe's chances in the big race?

Caf I think your chances of living are nil if you don't belt up, Bazzer! *(To Joe)* You divvy!

Joe Urrrrrrrrrr!

Caf How're you supposed to race Meltin' Ice Cream now?

Yakki It wasn't Joe, it was the bike . . .

Caf Excuses, excuses . . .

Bazzer Told you we should've had a pit stop.

Caf I'll throttle you! What're we gonna do now? Big Mal's lot'll be laughin' their heads off.

*The **Tigers** begin to argue amongst themselves.*

Joe My brother's got a bike.

They all shut up and stare at him.

Joe I'll ride that.

Bazzer What, that new one that looks like a bullet on wheels? You can't take that . . . he'll do you, won't he?

Joe *(Nods)* He said, if I ever touched it, he'd cut my liver out with a hedge trimmer.

Caf Well then.

Joe That's okay, Caf. There comes a time when a man's gotta do what a man's gotta do.

***Joe** marches off.*

Caf *(To Bazzer)* He's getting as daft as you.

***Caf** and the others pick up the gear and go off dejectedly. **Bazzer** remains.*

Bazzer *(As Murray Walker)* Well, plenty of excitement this week. Join us again next week for the final race of the season where . . . *(He realizes he is talking to himself)* Oi! Wait for me.

***Bazzer** runs off after the others.*

. . . .

Scene 5

*The back room of Mr Ali's shop. There is a big cardboard box in the room. **Caf** and **DG** enter, arguing. The others trudge in behind. **Joe** is not among them.*

Caf I don't know why I listen to you. I should never have let you talk me into this . . .

DG It's not my fault Joe wrecked his bike . . .

Caf Oh, belt up, DG. Okay, I'll tell Mal . . .

***Big Mal** and **Spanner** enter.*

Big Mal Tell me what?

Caf What're you doin' here?

Big Mal That isn't very polite, Caferine . . . just paying a friendly visit.

Caf Oh yeah?

Spanner Well, we did happen to hear that your hot shot biker has done his bike in!

Caf Did you? *(She glares at **DG** who looks innocent.)*

Big Mal So, if you want to call off the meet, I shall quite understand.

Caf Will you?

Big Mal We get the street, of course. By default.

Caf Listen, you clowns, we'll be at the crem, and you'd better be there too or we'll get the street by de-de-wotsit, and Joe'll still thrash your rider, even if he has to do the course on roller skates.

*The **Tigers** cheer.*

Big Mal As you wish, Caferine. If you lot want to make yourselves look a bunch of right wallies, we are only too happy to oblige. Cheerio.

***Big Mal** and **Spanner** go.*

Caf Right, Joe's going to ride his brother's bike, and we've got to make sure he gets it. Where's he keep it?

Yakki In his dad's shed, and he sleeps with the key under his pillow.

Bazzer We'll have to get Tealeaf to do a Mata Hari.

Tealeaf A what?

Bazzer Mata Hari. She was a spy . . . she'd lure men to her in flimsy nighties.

Tealeaf What were the men wearing flimsy nighties for?

Bazzer No, *she* wore the flimsy nighties, then she'd bash them on the head and run off with the secret plans.

Tealeaf I'll bash you on the head in a minute.

DG I've got an idea . . .

Caf I've had enough of your ideas!

Sharon I think we should leave Joe's brother's bike alone.

Others *(Together)* Shut up!

Joe's brother *bursts into the shop like a tornado.*

Brother Where is he!

Caf Who's this?

Yakki Joe's brother.

Bazzer Ooeeerr!!

Caf Has Joe done something?

Brother Oh, not a lot. Just put his nasty, filthy, sneakin' little paws on my Kwaker AR50, that's all. Just nicked my eight-hundred-quid motorbike! I've been savin' up for it since I was fourteen. I've had it three weeks and he's nicked it. *Where is he?!*

Caf He's not been in tonight.

Brother *(Suspiciously)* You sure?

Caf Yeah, positive.

Brother Well, you tell him that if he brings my bike back in totally brilliant nick, then I'll only kill him . . .

Sharon Only?

Brother But if he marks it, if he puts one tiny dent in it, if he scratches the paintwork the teeniest little bit, I'll have his skin off him, a bit at a time, and then I'll gouge his eyeballs out and cut his ears off and pull out all his fingernails and toenails one by one and then, I'll get *nasty!*

Sharon I think I'm going to be sick!

Brother You tell him, right?

Caf Yeah, course.

Joe's brother *storms off, the* ***Tigers*** *all breathe sighs of relief.*

Bazzer I thought he'd be upset.

Caf Upset?! Look, we've got to get Joe . . . tell him to hide up till tomorrow, or he's catmeat.

Joe *(Inside the box)* Has he gone?

The ***Tigers*** *react with shock.*

Caf Wossat?

Rodge-ah It's Joe . . . in the box.

Caf What are you doin' there? Get out!

Joe *gets out of the box, shaking like a leaf.*

Joe Is it safe?

Shammy How long have you been in there?

Joe Dunno. About half an hour.

Rodge-ah Why?

Joe Hiding from him.

Caf Look, I don't wanna lose but we can't let Joe get done in . . . we'll get his brother's bike back. *(**Joe** moans.)* Wait till he's calmed down, then Joe can go home.

Tealeaf Come on, Joe, where's the bike?

Joe In the canal.

Bazzer *(Offering his hand)* It was nice knowing you, Joe.

Rodge-ah You useless great . . .

Joe It wasn't *my* fault. It's a lot faster than my Vespa. I just twitched the throttle a bit and suddenly I've got the handlebars round me ear'oles and I'm going fast and I suppose I should have zigged when I zagged, 'cos I came off and the bike ended up in the canal, goin' bubble, bubble, bubble . . .

***Mr Ali** enters but no one notices.*

Shammy That's it, then. No bike, and no Joe either!

Tealeaf Not if his brother catches him. It'd be difficult riding with both arms and legs in plaster!

Mr Ali *(Sharply)* What is going on here? Joe, your brother just stopped me outside, wanting to know where you were because you'd stolen his bike . . . that's not like you. What's going on?

*The **Tigers** shuffle, saying nothing.*

Mr Ali DG?

***DG** looks at Caf and says nothing.*

Mr Ali Roger?

Rodge-ah *(Also looks at Caf, then, defiantly)* Caf bet Big Mal that Joe could beat the fastest kid from Eggie Harris's shop in a race round the crematorium.

Mr Ali Round the *what?*

Rodge-ah Joe's engine blew up so he stole . . .

Caf Borrowed!

Rodge-ah . . . Borrowed his brother's bike to race with, only he put it in the canal. It was nothing to do with me, Mr Ali.

Caf You wimp!

Mr Ali Well, Catherine?

Caf Like he said . . . the bet was to decide who got Coleman Crescent. We were doing it for you.

Mr Ali Listen, Catherine. Don't try to excuse your irresponsible behaviour by pretending you were acting to help me . . .

Caf But we were!

Mr Ali I said we needed customers on Coleman Crescent, I never said you should start a war to get it . . . a motorcycle race! Someone could have been killed! And round the crematorium of all places! Now listen, all of you, I absolutely forbid you . . .

Caf All right! Keep your Y-fronts on! It *was* for you. But it doesn't matter, 'cos Joe's wrecked his Vespa (***Joe's brother** enters)* and his brother's bike is at the bottom of the canal . . .

Brother WHHHHAAAAAAAAAAAAAATTTTTTTTT!

Yakki Run for it, Joe!

Joe I'm sorry, it was an accident . . .

Brother There'll be an accident when I get hold of you.

Sharon Leave him alone. Never mind about your bike, what about Joe? He could have been killed!

Brother It would've saved me a job!

***Brother** and **Joe** circle the box. **Joe** keeps it between them.*

Brother Come here . . .

***Caf, Shammy, Tealeaf** and **Yakki** grab the box and drop it over Joe's brother's head.*

Tealeaf Run, Joe!

***Joe** dives out of the room. **Joe's brother** rips the box to shreds and dives out after him. The **Tigers** follow in pursuit.*

Mr Ali *(Calling after them)* Catherine, just forget about this race, do you hear? DG! Pauline! Barry! Come back here!

***Mr Ali** follows them out.*

. . . .

Scene 6

*The crematorium. The **Tigers** (except Joe, Bazzer and Sharon) troop on carrying their racing gear. They are fed up.*

Shammy Oh, come on, Caf, this is a real waste of time.

Caf Shut up and gimme the flags.

Shammy What's the point? Joe's not coming and even if he does, what's he going to do? Let's forget it. I'll go round Coleman Crescent and get some customers for Mr Ali.

Caf If we lose this race . . .

Shammy There isn't going to *be* a race!

Caf If we lose this race and you go poachin' on Big Mal's territory, you'll come home with your head in a sling and your teef in a bag. Joe's got to turn up. I'll kill him if he doesn't.

Rodge-ah If his brother doesn't kill him first.

Caf You can shut up too, wimp. You had to go and tell Ali what was going off, didn't you?

Rodge-ah Well, I think it's disrespectful having a race round the crematorium. My father says . . .

Caf *Shut up!* Oh heck, here comes trouble.

***Mr Ali** enters. He looks grim-faced. He glares at the Tigers.*

Mr Ali Where's Joe?

Caf *(Sulkily)* Not 'ere.

Mr Ali That's just as well. At least Joe has some sense.

Caf Ha!

Mr Ali Sense enough not to take part in this foolish race. Don't you understand how dangerous motor racing can be? And around the crematorium . . . It's disrespectful.

Rodge-ah *(Quietly)* That's what I said.

DG What's it matter to you? You're a Muslim, anyway.

Others *(Together)* Shut up, DG!

Mr Ali Yes I am, but that makes no difference. Everyone should respect the dead . . .

DG What, gonna hear us, are they?

Mr Ali No, they're not, but others are: parents, friends, husbands, wives, children, coming here to remember their loved ones, only to find that you've turned it into some kind of race track.

Tealeaf Well, what are we supposed to do? Where else can we go? We're not allowed on the streets, so we've come here 'cos there's no one about this time of the morning.

Caf Yeah, we're always being told what we can't do, why don't you old crumblies tell us what we *can* do for a change?

Yakki Caf's right, Mr Ali. I mean, the coppers stopped us having a punch up with Big Mal's gang. But we both want the same thing so how are we supposed to decide who gets it?

Mr Ali Er . . . well, there are other ways. Negotiation, for instance.

Tealeaf *(Scornfully)* Negotiation!

Mr Ali Yes, why not? You can solve most things by talking.

Caf You can't talk to that lot!

Mr Ali Everybody who's ever started a war said much the same thing.

***Bazzer** rushes in. He is very proud of himself.*

Bazzer All ready, everyone? Come on, Guts, don't be shy . . .

***Sharon** comes in. She is 'wearing' an enormous oil can (a big cardboard box with a handle on one shoulder and a filler on the* *other). She is carrying a wreath of some description, a can of coke and a sash with 'winner' written on it.*

Caf What on earth are you doing?

Sharon Bazzer made me put it on. He said that the sponsors demanded it.

Shammy What sponsors?

Bazzer Er, Sid's garage . . . Well, he's not sponsoring us exactly, I just borrowed this to make the whole thing more realistic.

Caf *Realistic?* Guts dressed up in an oil can?

Bazzer It's for the presentation. Go on, Guts, do your speech.

Sharon *(Reluctantly)* I declare that the winner of the race is . . . whoever it is . . . and then I put the sash and the wreath over his head and Bazzer says that I've got to kiss him, but I don't fancy that . . .

Shammy That understandable. What if it's Meltin'?

Tealeaf What if it's Joe? Yuk!!

Caf Where is Joe?

Yakki Dunno, but here come the opposition.

Big Mal's gang *enter.* ***Meltin'*** *is in the middle of the group, dressed in full biking leathers. He is already doing his 'I am the greatest' victory waves. Someone has a ghetto blaster playing suitable music for a grand entrance.*

Big Mal Well, Caferine, where's Joe? Not here? Tut, tut, too bad. Meltin' was looking forward to burning him off.

Spanner Looks like he's chickened out.

Big Mal It certainly does. So, are you ready to give in?

__Caf__ looks at the rest of the Tigers. She hangs her head. She is about to speak when suddenly . . .

Yakki Look, it's Joe. He's turned up!

The __Tigers__ manage a feeble cheer but __Big Mal's gang__ just laugh.

Big Mal I see Joe, but I don't see a motorbike.

__Joe__ enters riding his BMX. He is filthy and breathing heavily.

Caf I've gotta talk to Joe.

Big Mal Don't take too long, will you, we've got to get to Coleman Crescent to get some new customers.

__Big Mal__ and __his gang__ move away.

Caf You look as though you've slept in a shed.

Joe I have! My gran's coal shed. Hidin' from my brother.

Caf Have you got a bike?

__Joe__ shakes his head.

That's it then, we'll have to give in.

Joe No! *(Runs to Meltin'.)* Hey Meltin', how about you and me havin' a time trial? We both use your bike, time it and the fastest time wins. Okay?

Meltin' You must be joking!

Spannor If you want to race Meltin', you'll have to do it on your BMX.

__Mal's gang__ laugh.

Joe *(Desperately)* Okay!

Tealeaf Shut him up, Caf, it's embarrassing.

Caf What've we got to lose?

Big Mal Now let's not be ridiculous . . .

Joe What's up? Scared?

Meltin' *(With a big grin)* I don't mind.

Big Mal Very well, Caferine, we accept. Meltin's Honda versus Joe's BMX. Okay?

Caf *grits her teeth and nods.*

Mr Ali I forbid this!

Mr Ali *and* ***Shammy*** *move away and have a furious argument out of earshot.* ***Joe*** *and* ***Meltin'*** *get ready.*

Bazzer Marshals, pit crew, get your flags and get to your places. Ready, Caf? *(As Murray Walker)* Well, here we are at the Silverstone Crem, the sun's beating down *(**Mal's gang** stop what they're doing and stare at him)* and we're in for a great race today. What do you think, Barry? *(As himself)* Well I . . . *(As Murray Walker)* Incredible! Let's see if I can have a word with the riders . . . *(He goes over to pester **Joe** and **Meltin'** who push him away.)*

Big Mal What's he doing?

Caf Commentating.

Big Mal Ah. What's she doing? *(He points at Sharon)*

Caf She's doing the presentations.

Big Mal Ah. *(Pause)* You have some strange friends, Caferine.

Caf I know.

Bazzer *(As Murray Walker)* Well, the riders are getting ready so, yes, I think the starter's ready. *(Own voice)* Got the flags, Caf? *(She nods)* On your marks.

***Joe** takes up a sprint start position, **Meltin'** lounges about.*

Get set, go!

***Caf** waves the Union Jack, **Joe** belts off, **Meltin'** strolls behind, hands in pockets. The **Tigers** encourage Joe. **Mal's gang** jeer.*

Bazzer *(As Murray Walker)* And Joe's away, down the straight, his little legs going like the clappers, and Meltin's just reached his bike . . .

Caf Don't let it start, God, please . . .

The motorcycle engine starts.

Bazzer And the engine roars into life.

Caf Thanks a lot, God.

Bazzer And Meltin's away, Joe looks over his shoulder as he pedals up the hill, past George-and-Mary-Dyson-Only-Sleeping, and Meltin' Ice Cream sweeps past . . .

Caf Bazzer, shut up before I murder you.

Sharon Well, that's that. Look at Meltin', he's halfway round before Joe's got to the second bend.

Tealeaf Let's hope he comes off on the coke.

*Pause. **Tigers** hold their breath, then groan.*

Caf No such luck, he's through okay. Into the finishing straight and Joe's still at the Chapel of Rest. We might as well go home now . . .

Tealeaf Hang on! There's something up . . . he's slowing up . . . he's stopped! *(The motorcycle engine noise dies away)* His chain's come off!

__Mal's gang__ groan and go frantic with worry.

Caf I take it all back, God.

Tealeaf He's started running. Come on, Joe!

__Tealeaf, Sharon, Caf__ and __Rodge-ah__ cheer on Joe. Even __Mr Ali__ begins to join in. __DG__ looks worried. __Meltin' Ice Cream__ runs on and past his __gang__, who cheer, and past the __Tigers__ who jeer. __Joe__ appears a couple of seconds behind. Before he can overtake Meltin', though, __DG__ steps in front of Joe with a 'Lollipop' stop sign. __Joe__ puts the brakes on hard.

Joe What the . . .

DG Pit stop.

Caf *Pit stop!* Are you out of your skull?

DG *(Innocently)* Gotta have a pit stop, Bazzer said.

Bazzer Oh yeah. I'll check his tyres.

While everyone's attention is on Bazzer, __DG__ quickly shields the front wheel with his body and does something to the front of the bike.

Bazzer You check his chain, Caf.

Caf *(Furious)* Get away from there! *(To DG)* And what are *you* doin'?

DG Nothing.

Caf Well, get away then. Joe, get a move on, *now!*

__Joe__ pedals off. The __Tigers__ cheer. __Mal's gang__ boo.

Tealeaf He's catching up with Meltin', only a few yards . . . hey! what's the matter?

Caf It's his handlebars . . . they've come loose or something. He's wobbling all over the place . . . oh no!

Tealeaf *(Awed)* Right over the handlebars.

Mal's gang *cheer.*

Bazzer He's landed on top of Abigail-Jones-Called-To-Glory.

Mr Ali *(Guilty and worried)* I should've stopped him. Do you think he's all right?

Caf 'Course he is. Get up, you great wazzock! Run!

Tealeaf It's all that training. He's shattered, he can't run.

Caf Come on, you great lump!

Bazzer Hang on, who's that on top of the hill?

Caf He's wavin' his arms about. Hey, it's Joe's brother!

Brother *(Miles away) JOE!* I'm coming to get you!

Tealeaf Joe's seen him. Cor, look at him go!

Bazzer His brother's catching him.

Caf Never mind that, Joe's catching Meltin' Ice Cream. Go on, Joe, you've got him . . . he's level . . . he's past . . . he's gonna win! GO ON JOE!

Joe *belts on to the finishing line. The* ***Tigers*** *cheer.* ***Mr Ali*** *laughs.* ***Caf*** *waves the chequered flag.* ***Sharon*** *tries to stop Joe but fails.*

Sharon I declare the winner is . . .

Joe *rushes past, not stopping.*

Caf He's done it! He's won!

Mr Ali Well done, Joe!

Bazzer *(As Murray Walker)* What an astonishing end to this race . . .

Tealeaf He's still going strong!

Meltin' *staggers on to a hostile reception from* ***Mal's gang.***

Big Mal You useless great nurk.

The other **Tigers** *come in, cheering.*

Bazzer This calls for a celebration!

He grabs the wreath from Sharon and jams it over Caf's head. He grabs the coke and shakes it up.

Caf What do you think you're doin'?

Bazzer The winner always does this with champagne after the race.

He pulls the can ring, just as **Joe's brother** *comes on.* **Brother** *gets a face full of coke as* **Caf** *ducks.* **Joe's brother** *turns to Bazzer.*

Brother *WOOOOOOOOOOOOOOAAAAAARRRRGGGGGGHHHHH*!

Bazzer Help!

Bazzer *runs off with* **Joe's brother** *in hot pursuit. The* **Tigers** *chase after them both.*

Mr Ali *(Watching them go)* Never a dull moment with this lot.

He goes.

Scene 7

The back room of Mr Ali's shop. ***Mr Ali*** *and the* ***Tigers*** *(except* ***Joe****) enter.*

Mr Ali All right, you lot. Let's get something straight. I know you want to keep your jobs . . .

Caf *(Sulkily)* It wasn't just that.

Mr Ali *(More kindly)* . . . and I appreciate you were trying to help me. I'm touched. Really. But you must never get involved in violence or danger on my behalf.

Bazzer Eh?

Mr Ali To help me, I mean. No punch ups. No races. All right?

The ***Tigers*** *mutter reluctant agreement.*

Mr Ali Right, now we've got to find a way to get Joe out of this fix . . .

Big Mal, Psycho *and* ***Spanner*** *storm in.*

Big Mal We want a word with you, Mr Ali. Don't think that you're getting the street, just because Joe won.

Mr Ali *You* insisted the race should go on.

Caf Listen you, Joe won, so we get the street.

Spanner It wasn't a fair race.

Mr Ali There is another way to decide who gets the new street.

Big Mal *(Suspicious)* What's that then?

Mr Ali Negotiation.

The ***Tigers*** *groan.*

Caf You'll give it all away!

Mr Ali Joe did win the race but I'm offering you a fair deal.

Big Mal What sort of deal?

Mr Ali A split. Fifty-fifty, straight down the middle. We take the odd numbers, you take the evens.

*The **Tigers** groan.*

Big Mal Er . . . well, maybe . . . all right. But *we* get the odd numbers.

Mr Ali Now wait a minute . . .

Big Mal Those are my terms. We get the odd numbers, or no deal.

Mr Ali *(Very reluctantly)* Oh, very well.

***Mal's gang** cheer. **Big Mal** looks pleased with himself.*

Big Mal Pleasure doing business with you.

***Mal** and his **gang** go. The **Tigers** sulk.*

Mr Ali What's wrong with you?

Caf We won the whole street, and you go and give half of it away.

Mr Ali You didn't *win* anything. Joe's brother has lost his bike, Joe's in big trouble, and either he or Meltin' Ice Cream could've been hurt, all because of this stupid race. And as for giving away Coleman Crescent, have you been there?

Caf Yeah, we all have.

Mr Ali But didn't you notice the numbers?

Tealeaf What're you on about?

Mr Ali It's called Coleman *Crescent* because of its shape. It's in the shape of a crescent – a half circle. There are twice as many houses on the outside as on the inside.

Shammy And the even numbered houses are on the outside! That's brilliant!

Caf	But you said you wanted the *odd* numbered houses.
Mr Ali	Of course. I had to give Malcolm something to argue about. He couldn't argue about a fifty-fifty split, but he couldn't agree without arguing or he'd lose face.
Sharon	Lose what?
Mr Ali	I mean, he'd look silly. Besides, he suspected a catch, so when I insisted on odd numbers he thought there must be one and so demanded that he had them. Which left us with the even numbers.
Caf	And twice as many houses as Big Mal. Wicked!
Shammy	And he can't complain when he finds out, 'cos he'll look stupid!
Mr Ali	Correct! You see, there are advantages to negotiation, especially when you take the trouble to make sure you know more than your opponent!
	The ***Tigers*** *laugh.* ***Joe*** *suddenly bursts in.*
Joe	Quick! Hide me! He's after me! He's got a pair of mole grips!
Sharon	What's he going to do with them?
Joe	I didn't stop to find out!
	Joe's brother *bursts in.*
Brother	Right, you little rat, I've got you. Somebody telephone for an ambulance and a few pints of blood.
Mr Ali	*(Calmly)* How is beating Joe up going to get your bike back?
Brother	It isn't, but if I don't beat him up, I still won't get it back, so I think I'll beat him up anyway, 'cos I'll enjoy it.
Mr Ali	Leave Joe alone and we'll get your bike back.
Brother	You can't. It's at the bottom of the canal.

Mr Ali Joe knows where it went. If you're nice to him, he might tell you.

Brother Nice? To *him*?!

Mr Ali And then, if you leave Joe alone, we'll all help you. We can grapple for it with hooks. It'll be easy to pull it out.

Brother Well . . . I s'pose . . . but who's gonna fix it, eh?

Mr Ali I will.

Yakki You don't know anything about bikes, Mr Ali.

Mr Ali Who says so? As a matter of fact, I used to be a motorbike mechanic. I'm sure that between us, Yakki, Joe and I can get your bike looking like new in a couple of days. I'll stop the money for spares out of Joe's wages. And when you've passed your test, I'll let you have a go on my bike.

Brother What is it?

Mr Ali A Norton 750.

Brother Yeah? Okay!

The ***Tigers*** *cheer.* ***Joe*** *sighs with relief.* ***Mr Ali*** *and* ***Joe's brother*** *shake hands.*

Mr Ali Come on, we can't stand here all day, there's work to be done. We can use the tow rope out of my car. We can nip round to the butchers to borrow a couple of meat hooks.

Bazzer I saw this film once where they were dredging the canal, and they found this rotting corpse . . .

Caf Shut up, Bazzer!

The ***Tigers*** *push him out of the door. Everyone goes except* ***Caf*** *and* ***DG****. She is staring at him, very hard.*

Caf What happened to Joe's BMX?

DG What are you on about?

Caf How did his handlebars get loose?

DG How do I know? I never touched them . . .

Caf You called that pit stop.

DG I got confused.

Caf Eggie Harris didn't bribe you to make sure that Meltin' won, did he?

DG Course not! What's up with you? Making accusations.

Caf I wonder why? Who was it who told us Ali was dealing in drugs and got me in trouble with the law? Whose idea was it to nick that baf? Who said we should challenge Mal to a race?

DG Well, everybody makes mistakes.

Caf You've made loads. I've got my eye on you.

__Caf__ goes. __DG__ lets out a whistle of relief. He stands thinking for a moment. He smiles, takes a five pound note out of his pocket and kisses it.

Caf *(Off)* You comin'?

__DG__ hurriedly puts the fiver back in his pocket.

DG Yeah, sure.

He goes. The room is empty.

Activities

What the authors say

We sat at a library table piled high with books. The librarian was glaring at us – he was going to have to put the books back on the shelves.

'Anything?'

'Not a sausage.'

'Well, that's because we're in a library, not a butchers!'

'Ha ha, very funny. I think all this searching has affected your brain. We need help.'

We called the librarian over.

'We're looking for a play.'

The librarian raised an eyebrow – the table was groaning under the weight of play scripts.

'These are no good.'

'No good?!' He looked amazed, and staggered a bit.

'No good for us. We want plays for lower seniors, you know. 11–14 year olds. Plays that are exciting, and lively, and fun.'

'Fun?' The librarian turned pale and looked as if he was about to faint. 'Why?'

'Because people learn more when they're enjoying themselves, and we want the people who read and act these plays to think about some of the important issues that affect their lives. . .'

'Ah,' he said, his face brightening, 'you want the philosophy section . . . two floors down. . .'

'No,' we said patiently, 'we want some plays that young people can understand, and enjoy reading and acting, and make them think about the world they live in.'

He must have heard the last bit. 'Geography?' he said hopefully. 'First floor. . .'

'No, plays,' we insisted.

He looked upset. 'But there are lots of plays here,' he grumbled. 'Shakespeare. . .'

'Wonderful stuff,' we said, 'but very complicated.'

'We've got Ibsen, Pinter, Chekhov, Shaw. . .'

'Yes, yes,' we interrupted, 'they're all great, but they're not suitable. They're all too difficult, or too dull. . . too long or too short. . .'

'What about this?' he held up a dog-eared, damp-stained book with triumph. The title was *Six Short Plays for Kiddiwinks.*

'Leave it out,' we begged.

He went all huffy. 'Since you're so difficult to please,' he snapped, 'why don't you go away and write something?'

We looked at each other. We looked at him.

'That's a good idea,' we said. 'Thanks.'

And we left him to get on with putting the books away.

We realized we had a problem. We'd need lots of copies of the plays, not just one. We would have to find a publisher. After looking through the yellow pages, we found the number of Oxford University Press. We rang them up (it felt a bit like ringing up Buckingham Palace) and explained that we wanted to do.

'Great,' they said. 'We'd like to publish them.'

But what were we going to write about? This was going to be tricky!

So we put our heads together (this must have looked rather odd) and invented some characters. This was done by thinking about real people and basing our characters on them. For instance, one character is based on a girl who was not afraid of pain and prided herself on being tough. Another was partly based on a boy who always talked about television and liked to be the class joker. Of course, we had to add lots more to them to create the characters of Caf and Bazzer. We also had to put these characters into situations which people could recognize. You have probably been in some of the situations that the characters find themselves in. Because of this we wanted to give people who would read the play and act it out, a chance to add their own experiences to it, so we decided to add a Do-it-Yourself section to each play.

Eventually, after a lot of hard work and rewriting (writers have to write out plays, stories, poems or essays several times in order to ge them just right – that's why your teacher gets you to do draft copies of work, before you present them as best) we completed the plays.

We took them to the publishers.

'Right,' said the publishers, 'are they enjoyable?'

'We think so,' we replied.

'Will they make people think?'

'We hope so,' we answered.

'Well, we'd better publish them and find out,' they decided. 'Just one more thing.'

'What's that?' we asked.

'Will you write an introduction to the plays, saying why you wrote them?'

'Hmmm,' we thought. 'That could be tricky . . .'

Steve Barlow and Steve Skidmore

Understanding the Plays

When we wrote these plays, we had to decide three things:

1 Who would be the characters in the play?
2 What would they say to each other?
3 What would happen to them?

We obviously wanted to make the plays enjoyable and fun to read and act out, but we also wanted to make *you* think about the way the characters behave.

We have done this by putting **clues** into each play which will help you to understand *why* the characters behave as they do. When you read these plays, you will have to be detectives. You will have to find these clues and be ready to produce them as evidence to back up your ideas about the play and the characters.

To help you in your detective work, the following pages contain suggestions of things you can do to explore the meaning of each play. All good detectives need methods to solve mysteries. Here are some of the methods you can use:

Improvisation

You are given a situation to work on in groups. Using your own words, you act out a scene which shows what you think about this subject. There are two main types of improvisation:

1. **Planned:** in this you are given time to prepare your work by talking with your friends and trying out your ideas. When you have practised your work and are satisfied with it, you show it to other people.
2. **Instant:** in this you are given a character and a situation, but you are not given any time to prepare. You must start the improvisation straight away.

Role Play

A situation is chosen, and every member of the group must pretend to be a character in that situation and act as that character would. For example, in a role play about a circus, members of the group would take on the roles of all the different characters you might see there: clowns, trapeze artists, acrobats, lion tamer, tightrope walker, etc.

Still Images

A still image is like a photograph. Any number of people may be in the image. A situation is chosen and the group must produce a frozen picture as if they had been captured on film by a photographer. You may wish to choose just one image, or use a series of images to tell a story.

Thought Banding

This helps us to understand what the characters in a still image are thinking. In turn, each member of the group says what their character was thinking at the moment the 'photograph' was taken.

Hot Seating

When a member of the group has played a character in an improvisation, a role play or a written play, they can be put in the 'hot seat'. This means that other members of the group can ask them questions, and they must answer *in the character* of the person they have just played.

Brainstorming

This can be done in small groups (using pen and paper) or as a full class (using a chalkboard or marker board, flipchart, etc). One member of the group is chosen to write down any comments the group makes about a play or a chosen topic. These can be single words or short sentences. Write down everything that is said no matter how silly it may sound. After a few minutes, look at the paper or board, and talk about what you have said.

Paper Tigers

Character

Here is a list of words:

bossy	awkward	crafty
honest	intelligent	stupid
crazy	dishonest	liar
daft	nervous	kind

List

Write down the names of three characters who appear in **Paper Tigers**. Choose some words which best describe each character and write these underneath the character's name.

Can you think of any other words to describe that character? If so, write these down.

When you have done this, you must find some evidence to support your ideas.

For example, if you think that Caf is bossy, you must try to prove this by finding speeches in the play when she shows that she is a bossy character.

Talk

Tell the rest of your class what words you have chosen to describe each character. Back up your arguments by reading out the evidence you have collected from the play.

Do others agree with you or have they found some evidence which disproves yours?

Write

Now choose one character and write a paragraph (about three or four sentences) to describe that character. Use the words you have chosen and the evidence you have discovered.

Theme

Yakki arrives at the paper shop and is almost immediately teased by Caf and the rest of the Tigers.

List

Make a list of the things they say to annoy and upset him.

Some of these are insulting only to Yakki, but some are insulting to anyone who comes from Wales. Divide your list into *personal comments* and *national comments*.

Mr Ali tries to help Yakki by telling him how he was treated when he first bought the paper shop.

List

Make a list of the things the Tigers say and do to annoy and upset Mr Ali.

Compare this list with the one you made for Yakki.

What differences can you find? Can you give any reasons for these differences?

Changing Schools

Survey

Make a survey of your class to find out how many members of the group have changed schools.

What did they feel like when they first arrived?

How did the other people in the school treat them?

Why were they treated like this?

What was the worst thing that happened to them?

When did they feel that they were accepted by other people?

Newcomers

Group Poem

As a whole class, brainstorm some words and short sentences, that describe how a newcomer feels.
After five minutes, divide into groups and choose eight to twelve words or sentences.

Write these down on separate pieces of paper.
As a group, arrange these into an order that everyone agrees with. You should try to make this as interesting as possible.

When you have agreed the order of the words, you may add others to connect up what you have arranged, to produce a poem.

When your group is satisfied with this, make a neat copy of your group poem and share it with the rest of the class, by reading it out and displaying it on the wall.

Write

A Stranger's Diary

Imagine that you have moved to a different country that is completely strange to you – or even to another planet! You have decided to keep a diary of what happens to you and how you feel in your new surroundings.

For example, the first day's entry in your diary might look like this:

> June 26th
>
> Arrived on Planet Spud. The people here speak a very strange language. I asked the first person I met the quickest way from the Spaceport to the Information Office, and he said something that sounded like, 'Pinch my rubber duck'. He also stuck his thumb in his left ear and waggled his fingers at me. I was later told this was the local way of saying, 'Hello, have a nice day'.

Write an entry in your diary for every day of your first week in your new home.

Map Making

Once you have begun to find your way about, you will need to make a map showing where all the important places are. Make this map as interesting as possible, with pictures and explanations.

Drama Ideas

1 Still Images

In small groups, create a **still image** that shows a newcomer being left out. **Thought band** each person in the photograph. What are they thinking and feeling?

2 Improvisation

Break into groups of four or five. Each group chooses one person to be a newcomer to the school.

Plan out and improvise the following scene:

> It is dinner time, in the school yard. Everyone, except the newcomer, is playing a game, or is talking.
>
> The newcomer must try to make friends with the others.
>
> The others should show the newcomer that she/he is not wanted.
>
> Finish the improvisation and change the person playing the part of the newcomer.

Do this until everyone has played the part of the newcomer.
Return to the large group and share your experiences.
How did you feel when you were the newcomer?

What was said to you?

What hurt you most of all?

What did you feel about the people who were teasing you?

How did you try to make friends with the others?

Was this successful?

3 Role Play

Choose a volunteer to be a newcomer to your school.
The rest of the group are members of a form.
The newcomer goes out of the room.
Your teacher then tells the rest of the group a piece of information about the newcomer, for example:

> The newcomer is very rich.
> The newcomer is poor at reading.
> The newcomer is from another country.

The newcomer's mother and father have just died.
The newcomer is physically handicapped.
The newcomer's mother is a famous film star.

The person playing the newcomer comes back into the room and sits down. Your teacher tells you to get on with some work and starts to mark books. How do you react to the newcomer?
Play out this situation.
Remember the teacher is still in the room!
After an agreed length of time, stop the role play and **hot seat** the newcomer. You may wish to ask some of the following questions:

Did they guess the piece of information the teacher gave?
How did they feel about the way the rest of the group behaved towards them?
Do they think that they would be able to settle in that group?
Was anyone especially nasty or kind towards them?
Why was this?

After you have finished hot seating the newcomer, change the person playing the newcomer. The teacher gives out a new piece of information about this character. Repeat the role play and the hot seating exercise. Do this as many times as you wish.

When you have finished all the role plays, discuss how you reacted to the different newcomers. Did the pieces of information that the teacher gave you make you act differently towards the various newcomers?

Caf's Baf

Character

In this play we meet three new characters: Mr Ali's mother, Mrs Roberts and the plumber. **Brainstorm** words that describe the type of characters they are. Use quotes and incidents from the play to back up your ideas.

Theme

At the end of **Paper Tigers**, Caf insults Mr Ali by calling him 'Curry Face'. At the end of **Caf's Baf**, DG calls Mr Ali 'Curry Face'. Caf reacts to this by threatening DG and telling him never to insult Mr Ali again. **Caf's Baf** is about the things that happen to make Caf question her reactions to Mr Ali and change her opinion of him.

Lying

Discuss

Most people have told a lie. Find out who in your group has told a lie in the past week. What was the lie?
Put the lies under the headings, such as:

To get out of trouble
To show off
Not to hurt someone else's feelings

What happened after the lie was told? Was it found out? What were the consequences?

Task

In the play, several people tell lies; some tell more than one. Use your detective skills to hunt down who tells a lie in the play.
Make a list of the characters, the lies they tell and the reasons they tell the lies.

Character	Lie	Reasons

Discuss

Compare your list with other members of the group. Do they have the same reasons? Can you work out every character's reasons for lying?

When DG says that he didn't ring the police can we be sure that he isn't lying? Are there any other instances when we aren't sure whether a character is telling the truth or not?

Prejudice

At first, Caf doesn't want to like Mr Ali. She seems to suggest that she is against him because of the colour of his skin. However, she can offer no *logical* explanation for her dislike. This type of *illogical* thought is called **prejudice**.

Talk

What types of prejudice are there? As a group, brainstorm these. Discuss the different forms of prejudice. Are you prejudiced against someone? Why?

Caf says that she thinks like she does, because her Mum thinks like that, and has influenced Caf's thoughts. A lot of prejudice is based on thoughts you may have because:

- your parents think them
- your friends think them
- you think you ought to think them
- 'responsible' people tell you that you ought to think them
- people you admire think them.

Think

Can you think of any more reasons why prejudice exists?

What makes Caf change her mind about Mr Ali?

Rumours

DG tells Caf that Mr Ali is a slum landlord and is going to make lots of money out of the people to whom he is going to rent the house. In **Paper Tigers**, some of the characters think that Mr Ali is a drugs dealer. These are not facts but are **rumours**.

Rumours can develop in different ways: they may start from being untrue, as in this play, or they may start out as being true stories but they change as they are passed on from one person to another. To show how this can happen try the following exercise:

Chinese Whispers

The group sits in a circle or a line. One person starts a message by whispering it to the person sitting next to them. This person then whispers it to the next person and so on until everyone has heard the message. The final person then tells the rest of the group what the message is. Then compare this with the original message.

It is important that you are only allowed to say the message *once* to the person sitting next to you.

The Senses

Caf stinks at the beginning of the play as she hasn't had a bath. She offends people's sense of smell.

SMELL is one of the five senses. The others are:
TASTE
TOUCH
SIGHT
HEARING

We can use these to create a *SENSES* poem.

Poetry

Pick up an object, for instance an orange.

Think of one of the senses, for example, *touch*. With your eyes closed, feel the orange and think of some words to describe its feel. Try and use as many unusual words or phrases as you can. This will make the poem more interesting. Then put these down on paper.
Do the same for the other four senses.
Then arrange the words and phrases you have written into an order with which you are happy. You will have created a total sense poem about an object.

Crime Report

Write

Imagine you are one of the police officers sent to investigate the theft of Mr Ali's bath. Write up a report describing what has happened.
You could begin:

Include your ideas about how the crime could have been committed and who you suspect.

Drama Ideas

1 Hot Seating

Hot seat Caf. Why does she have the argument with Shammy? Why is she sorry at the end of it? What was she feeling?
Hot seat Shammy. What did he think about the argument? What does he think of Caf?

2 Still Images

In small groups, create a picture that shows prejudice. When you have formed this image, **thought band** the people in the picture. What are they thinking and feeling at that particular moment?

3 Invent a Prejudice

A member of the group invents a prejudice. This must not be a well-known one, but must be made up by that person. For example, the person might dislike people with green eyes or people who wear black socks.

The rest of the group walk round the classroom talking to each other. The person who invented the prejudice also walks around and collects those people who are not included in the prejudice (who do not have green eyes or wear black socks) but without saying why. This will leave out several people who will then be ignored by the rest of the group.
After a few minutes, stop the walking and talk about prejudice.

You may repeat this by choosing a new person and a new prejudice. Remember that the person who has invented the prejudice should *not* reveal what it is until the very end. This will keep people guessing and wondering what it is.

4 Changing Emotions

Caf changes her views on Mr Ali. She also changes in her *feelings* towards him.
Work in pairs.
One person chooses an emotion (eg sadness).
The other person then chooses the opposite emotion (happiness).
Begin an improvisation which starts with Caf and Mr Ali displaying these emotions.
As the improvisation progresses, make the characters change their emotions to the opposite ones to those which they began with. Therefore if you were happy, you should be sad by the end of the improvisation.

A Burn Round the Crem

Character

Brainstorm words to describe the four characters we meet from Eggie Harris' gang: Big Mal, Psycho, Spanner and Meltin' Ice Cream. Remember to use lines and incidents from the play to back up your arguments.
Eggie Harris never appears in the play but we hear a lot about him.

FACT FILE

Name: Eggie Harris
Age: 53
Hair: None!
Height: 1.60m.
Eyes: Brown (wears spectacles)
Weight: 14½ stone (92.1 kg.)
Clothes: Usually wears dark trousers, white shirt and cardigan. Doesn't wear a tie.

Write

Use these facts to write a description of Eggie Harris. Add some of your own ideas about what he is like.
What are his likes and dislikes?
What does he think of other people?
Is he married?

Talk

Compare your description of him with ones written by other members of the group. Has anyone written a favourable description of him? If people have written an unfavourable one, can they say why?

Gangs

In the play, Big Mal's gang and the Tigers are rivals for Coleman Crescent. What exactly is a gang? Why do people join gangs? **Brainstorm** some ideas with the rest of the group.

Think

What gangs do you know about in your area? Are you in one? If you are, tell the rest of the group about it. What other gangs do you know of? Make a list of these, including ones from history, from other countries, and from TV, books, plays, etc.

What are the good points about belonging to a gang? Are there any bad points?

Treachery

The Tigers tell Mr Ali that they can't negotiate with Big Mal's gang because they can't trust them. Mr Ali replies that people who start wars say that the other side can't be trusted. Later, Mr Ali tricks Big Mal. Is this unfair? Give reasons for your answer. Do you think Big Mal would agree with you?

If you betray or let down a group of people who trust you, or if you help those people's enemies, you are a **traitor**. Who do you think is a traitor in the play? Give reasons for your answer.

Victims

Have you ever had anything stolen which you really cared about, like Joe's brother's bike? What did you feel like? What would you have done to the thief if you had caught them?

Talk

Discuss this with the rest of the group.

A Certain Age . . .

Joe owns a bike, but he is not allowed to ride it on the road until he is sixteen. There are many laws which stop you doing things legally, until you are a certain age.
Copy this table and find out the information to complete it:

LAW	THE AGE YOU MUST BE
Drink alcohol in a pub	
Can ride a moped	
Go to a PG film	
Get married	
Vote	
Drive a car	

Talk

Do you think it is fair that there are laws stopping you doing things until you are a certain age?
Would you change any of these ages?
Discuss your thoughts with the rest of the group.

Race Game

By using the information in the play and your own ideas, invent a game based on the race course round the 'Crem' or some other place known to you. You could work on your own or with a group of friends.

You will need paper, card, dice and counters. Draw out the circuit and divide it into numbered squares. On these you can write in hazards, such as YOU HIT THE COKE PILE – GO BACK THREE SQUARES and bonuses, such as YOUR VISOR CLEARS – GO FORWARD THREE SQUARES.

When you have drawn out the circuit, and made the counters, write down the rules of the game. Make sure the rules are clear, so that other people can understand and play the game.

Get someone else to try out your game. If they can't understand it, then you should re-write the rules in order to make them clearer.

Drama Ideas

1 Hot Seating

Use the hot seating technique in order to discover more about what the characters think in the play.

Hot seat:
- Big Mal
- Joe's brother
- Joe
- Caf
- Eggie Harris
- Mr Ali

What did they think about the race? Was the outcome satisfactory? Were they worried at any time? What do *they* think about the other characters?

2 Negotiation

Work in threes and name yourself **A, B, C.**
As have a disagreement with **B**s. For example they might be neighbours and **A** thinks that **B** plays their stereo far too loud.
Cs are counsellors – they are going to listen to both sides' arguments.

As present their argument.
Bs then reply to this, presenting *their* side of the story.
Cs then have to try and negotiate a satisfactory agreement by presenting a settlement to the argument that all sides are happy with.

When you have done this, discuss the results.
Then swap roles and let someone else be the counsellor.